Bemelmans

ALSO BY LUDWIG BEMELMANS:

Hotel Splendide

The Donkey Inside

Small Beer

Life Class

My War with the
United States

I LOVE YOU

I LOVE YOU

I LOVE YOU

LUDWIG BEMELMANS

NEW YORK : THE VIKING PRESS : 1942

ACKNOWLEDGMENT IS MADE TO
HARPER'S BAZAAR, THE NEW YORKER,
TOWN AND COUNTRY, AND *VOGUE,*
IN WHICH SOME OF THESE STORIES
FIRST APPEARED

PUBLISHED IN SEPTEMBER 1942
SECOND PRINTING SEPTEMBER 1942
THIRD PRINTING SEPTEMBER 1942
FOURTH PRINTING OCTOBER 1942
FIFTH PRINTING OCTOBER 1942

42 - 20660

PRINTED IN U. S. A. BY
AMERICAN BOOK-STRATFORD PRESS
PUBLISHED ON THE SAME DAY IN THE DOMINION OF
CANADA BY THE MACMILLAN COMPANY OF CANADA
LIMITED

CONTENTS

SOUVENIR

SOUVENIR

Every time I pass, along the West Side Highway, a spot just above Forty-Sixth Street, there comes over me the feeling that I experience at the dentist's as I wait for him to get through putting the little drill in his machine, the sorrow of saying good-by, and the sadness of a band playing far away, all rolled into one. It's the stretch where you can look down on the *Normandie*. I am glad to report that workers are busy righting her. The superstructure is gone and on the side over the de luxe cabins are planks and lampposts. It looks as if a street stretched over the water, over the ship—a strange thing to contemplate, a fantastic scene.

I have always given more affection to the *Normandie* than to any other ship. I loved her for her gaiety, for her color, for that familiarity with all the world that was her passenger list. In her décor she leaned toward excess; there was something of the *femme fatale* about her. She assumed a seigneur's privilege of frowning on the lesser, fatter, slower, and more solid boats. Like all aristocrats, she had abominable moods. I think she was more female than all the other ships that I have known. I think that's why I loved her so.

We traveled on her once under extraordinary circumstances. We intended to spend a year in Europe. I had booked passage on her and was ready to sail when an eager young man with an extensive vocabulary came to see me. He told me that the French Line was delighted to have us cross on the *Normandie*, that its directors wished to make everything very comfortable for us, and that instead of giving us just an ordinary cabin, they were glad to be able to offer us a *suite de luxe*. I am not one to sleep on a hard mattress when I can have a soft one, so the young man and I bowed to each other and had three Martinis each. I went to Mark Cross and bought a set of new trunks to go with the better accommodations and had my tie pressed. We also invited a lot of people to see us off.

It seemed that at the last moment all the ordinary cabins *de luxe* had been taken and the only thing left to do with us was to put us into one of the *Suites de Grand Luxe*. We went into a palace called Trouville—private terrace, servants' dining-room, feudal furniture. Everybody was satisfied, particularly with the Lalique ashtrays.

The next morning I sat in my *dodine* rocking on my private terrace and regarding the morning sun and the sea. After five minutes of the most profound rocking,

and of the most profound silence, except for the rocking, I thought I would burst with rage when a man appeared on my private terrace and stood there, looking out to sea.

I shouted, "Excuse me, but I don't think we have met."

"Oh, I'm so sorry. I just came out," said the man.

"Do you happen to know that this is my private terrace *alors?*" I said to him.

"Oh, I'm so sorry. I'm just admiring the view," he said and turned away. I kept on rocking. He walked over to his own private terrace. He was introduced to me later as the banker Jules Bache.

The day after sailing, the great hall, crowded the night before with good-by sayers, messenger boys, pickpockets and weeping relatives, was now swept clean. The runners had been taken up, the furniture put back in place. The room of silver, gold, and glass, large as a theater, floated through the ever clean, endless ocean outside the high windows. In a corner, a steward who looked like Sacha Guitry was arranging French stamps in boxes and straightening out the writing paper. Up on the sun deck, children were riding the merry-go-round that was built inside of the first funnel. On the outside of that funnel was a small plaque. It was like the charm on a bracelet, elegant and right. On it was inscribed: *Normandie—Chantiers Penhoet, Saint Nazaire*—and the date she was built. *Chantiers* is a lovely name for a shipyard. It sounds like a song, like the name of a beautiful song-bird.

There was a dark fortress of a woman on board that voyage, an old countess with a face made of Roquefort and eyes like marbles, the kind of marbles that boys call "aggies." She sat wrapped in her sables in the front row of three lines of deck chairs outside the main Salon. On her lap, covered by a small hound's-tooth blanket, asthmatic and dribbly, sat a Pekinese with thyroid trouble; his eyes were completely outside of his head. Whenever my daughter Barbara passed by her chair, the old countess lifted the blanket, gave the dog, whose name was Piche, a little push, and said to him, *"Piche, regardez donc la petite fille qu'elle est mignonne!"* One day she reached out her hand, but Barbara ducked and ran all the way to the Trouville Suite nursery where she burst into tears.

The other outstanding figure on that trip was a young widow. She was dressed in long, glamour-girl blond hair and black satin. I think she rubbed herself with a lotion every morning, and then pasted her clothes on her body; there wasn't a wrinkle in them. A doctor could have examined her as she was. Her arms were weighed down with bracelets, all of them genuine, and of course she had a silver fox jacket. An icebox full of orchids helped her bear up throughout the voyage. She appeared with fresh flowers at every meal, and she had with her a sad pale little girl, who was not allowed to play with other children. She wore a little mink coat on deck—the only junior mink I have ever seen.

The way the young widow managed her entrances into the dining-room reminded me of Easter at the Music Hall. She waited until the orchestra played Ravel's *Bolero* and then she came, surrounded by expensive vapors, heavy-lidded, the play of every muscle visible as a python's. At the first landing of the long stairs she bent down, while everyone held their breath, until she succeeded in picking up the train of her dress. Then a faultless ten inches of calf and ankle came into view and, with industrious little steps, she climbed down the rest of the stairs to the restaurant. Once seated, she smeared caviar on pieces of toast and garnished them with whites of eggs until they looked like the cards one sends to the bereaved; with this she drank champagne and looked out over the ocean. The sad little girl said nothing the whole day long.

The last night on board, the widow fell out of her role. A beautiful, exquisitely modeled, long, slim, gartered leg came dangling down from a high-held knee, out of black satin and lingerie. She danced like Jane Avril and let out a wild cowboy "Whoopee," blowing kisses to everyone.

I think the tips on that voyage amounted to more than the whole price of the passage. I have never enjoyed such service. The elevator had not only one operator but a second man who squeezed himself into the cab, pushing the first one against the wall. Then he asked the passengers for their destination and handed this information on to the operator. He also opened the door and rushed ahead to guide us to whatever room we had asked for. The service was perfect, altogether too perfect. I ran into trouble because of its perfection several times. Once, when I went to arrange for railroad tickets, the bearded man standing inside the kiosk bowed, rubbed his hands, and asked me where I wanted to go after the ship docked. I said, "First to Paris, and then to Zuerrs in the Tirol." I ordered three tickets to Zuerrs. I said to him that Zuerrs was on top of the Arlberg between—but I got no further. He stopped me, and explained, "It is I, Monsieur, who will tell you where Zuerrs is found!"

Was there ever anything more real, more certain, than

the appearance of the Scilly Islands and Bishop's Rock when, at the end of the voyage, the mists began to take on a greenish tinge and slowly, out of them, came the cliffs and green hills of the English landscape?

Later, off Southampton, the *Normandie* turned into the wind, her propellers trembling as the engines idled. Baskets of Dover sole were brought on board, and a few people with ruddy complexions and sports clothes came up from the tender, to make the crossing over the Channel to France.

As we steamed slowly into Le Havre, the Sacha Guitry steward in the lounge put his stamps away and locked up the writing paper. Then came the most lenient customs inspection imaginable, and we found ourselves about to board the blue boat train for Paris. Instead of an engineer, the chef leaned out of the train, his white cap floating in the smoke of the engine.

When we arrived in Paris, we had to wait until they carried Danielle Darrieux off the train. The frugal French taxicab drivers almost threw their caps in the air when they saw her. They waved them with the greatest degree of abandon and enthusiasm, but they did not let them fly. We finally persuaded one to take us and our baggage. It was impossible to go from the Trouville suite of the *Normandie* to the old Hotel de Nice on the Boulevard Montparnasse, or even to the respectable anonymity of the Saint-Georges-et-D'Albany. So we went to my favorite hotel in Europe, the Ritz, on the Place Vendôme. This rare mansion has the quality of making one feel it has been one's home for centuries. Its elegance is effortless. It might be the residence of an archbishop or a first class *maison close*. Its chief decorative features were the women's hats in its corridors, the garden, the porters, the waiters, the professional beauties, the young dancing men; the good and the bad made its pulses beat, its doors swing with *élan* and music. It had an imposing entrance on the Place Vendôme and a quiet one on the Rue Cambon. It had, of course, hand-churned butter, an excellent cellar and the model of all maîtres d'hôtel in the person of Olivier. It also had a nice set of prices.

One day in the third month that we stayed there, I sat looking out over the elegant tops of the fat cars below in the square while on my fingers I counted the money I had left. It seemed that most of it had simply disappeared, that the year in Europe would shrink to a short vacation, and we would never see Zuerrs in the Tirol.

That afternoon, after I had counted my money three times more, and during the process it had not increased, I went over to the French Line office.

"Look here," I said to the man at the counter, "I would like to have a return passage on the *Normandie*—a cabin for three people in the third class—somewhere near the linen room; an inside cabin, all the way down near the bottom of the ship, at the minimum rate."

He took my name and disappeared. I had seen him on

board several times on the way over. He came back looking extremely worried. It is hard to overdo an imitation
of a Frenchman when he is excited. The young man acted
like Lou Holtz telling a French joke, with gestures.

"*Non, non, mais non, non, Monsieur Bemelmans—
ça–ne–va–pas!*" He emphasized the last syllables sepa-
rately, exercising his eyebrows in double-quick time. Then
he spread out a first-class cabin plan. "We have orders,
Monsieur, to extend to you every courtesy. The suite in
which you came over happens to be free on the return
trip, and it is"—here he made a blue pencil mark, and a
princely gesture with his right hand—"hereby reserved

for you again, and at the same price you paid for your passage from New York, the price of an ordinary first class cabin."

"Look," I said—while he had his hands folded and both eyes closed—"I am a writer——"

"I know," he interrupted, flashing the palms of both hands, like two search-lights, "that is just why we wish you to write something very nice—*ah, la publicité, la publicité*—is very important. That is why we are glad to be of——"

"I am a writer," I continued, "but I do not write only about the *beau monde*. I also write about the simple life. I have found out how beautiful it is upstairs. Now I wish to go downstairs, you understand, and find out how it is down there."

He focused his attention on me by glaring at a red spot on the left side of my nose, where a French bee had stung me in the Jardin d'Acclimatation. He made a lance of his pencil, and pointing at me, he opened his mouth—but I got ahead of him.

"I now want to experience," I said, "how a man feels who has no money, or very little, and who has to eat and live in the third class."

"Ah," he replied, "Victor Hugo did not become a hunchback in order to write *Notre Dame de Paris*, and if Balzac had lived like Père Goriot . . ." I stopped him with an icy look, and he returned to a contemplation of my nose, folding his arms and waiting. When I had said my piece, he pushed the cabin plan so that the suite lay in front of me, and pointed at it with his pencil.

"It is all arranged," he said; "you will live in the suite, and every day someone will escort you to the third class, where you may observe life. For your repasts you will, of course, come back upstairs. Madame and the *bébé* will stay upstairs. It will mean a lot of writing and paper work, explanation and confusion, but that is what I am here for."

"Look," I began once more, "you must be very patient with me. I am a very simple person. My mind has chronic limitations. Furthermore, I belong to the ultra-realist school of writers. I want to experience the feelings of a man who is *obliged* to travel in the third class with his wife and child."

"*Enfin*," he shrugged his shoulders, "I have nothing to say." Hopelessly, he shoved the plan around and made the reservation. We sailed back in the third class later that summer.

I saw this man again, a short while ago. He was bent over another book of reservations, in a New York hotel.

"Tell me," he said, searching for the spot on my nose, "what did you find out on that trip? How was the third class?"

"Oh," I said, "I found that a glass of *vin ordinaire* is

good, and the *cuisine bourgeoise* is excellent; that the vibration and the pitching are bad. But there was a sharp-faced youngster who tasted ice cream for the first time, and ate himself sick on it. There was a man at our table with a wife and child and dirty finger-nails, who appeared on the Passenger List as Mr. and Mrs. Ginsberg and Infant Condé; and at the next table was a returning missionary who brought his own savages with him in the form of three children who had to be put out of the dining-room at almost every meal. There was also a beautiful girl and a young man who loved her. They were coming back from a trip, the *promenade obligatoire* through all the chateaux, cathedrals, ruins and galleries of France. They believed in themselves and in the little book in which they had the names and dates of everything. They could never let each other alone. There was a man in a sweater and cap who had left his home, his business, and a fortune of several million marks behind when he was dragged out of bed one night by the Gestapo. He still hid himself behind ventilators and sneaked along the corridors. He was a sick man when he came on board. He sat alone and ate alone, his eyes always looking down. He was still followed by ghosts. He clung to the side of the deck-house, when he walked outside, or stood alone on the deck. He seemed to apologize for his own presence. He was afraid that it would all end and from somewhere a hand would seize him and drag him back into his misery. Slowly,

he began to heal. . . . The last day, I saw him look up. He smiled.

"We also had the honor of having at our table a detective from the uniformed force of the New York Police Department. He was a wonderful man, as big as a house, with a heart of gold and a hand-shake that hurt for three hours. He had been on a real busman's holiday, inspected jails, police stations, crime bureaus and disorderly houses. He spoke like a radio program. He was like a book that opened at the beginning of every meal and closed again

21

when he left the table. He lived his life more successfully than any man I have ever met. I think he was really a happy man, the happiest man I have ever known. He lacked the mechanism for being otherwise.

"This enviable functionary must be allowed to express himself. I took down his dinner conversation of Friday. Listen:

" 'Well, this goil I was telling you about, Virginia di Milo, traded the love and security of a good home to become a glamour actress in Hollywood. She ran away with a rat named Max, who promised to make a star out of her. He just posed as a director. In real life, the poor goil was Goitrude Schmitt from Brooklyn.

" 'I was born in Brooklyn, too, and I was raised in Brooklyn, went through kindergarten and grammar school there and right up through Adelphi Academy. My father was a Republican, but he believed in Wilson. He was like a fish out of water and I guess that's where I get my idealism from. Take Roosevelt! If something happened to that man I think I'd have a real crying spell. I feel about him the way I did about my father. He's a gentleman. My old man was kind, too, but when somebody didn't do the right thing he could slug, just like Roosevelt. . . .

" 'Well, Goitrude Schmitt was dead of malnutrition in a cheap rooming house when she met her end, and the last scene was in the home of a broken-hearted mother in

Brooklyn, who had come down looking for her, running through the Missing Persons Bureau, but it was too late. . . . That rat, Max, who was responsible for all this, who lured her away and brought her to a life of shame, landed in jail, and we, the detectives of this department which has brought him to justice, hope they'll throw away the key. . . .

" 'Now I hope you'll understand this story and take it to heart. Don't disappear, don't be a vanishing American. Good Evening.'

"There was hardly a dry eye in the room as he got up and went, with six Catholic priests, to see Betty Boop in the third class movies.

"I remember, too, half a dozen athletic young Americans who used the ship as a gymnasium, despite the purposes of its builders and all the restraining efforts of the crew. They managed to appear one night in dinner clothes, with their girls, up in the first class. . . . Oh, it was all a lot of fun on the *Normandie*, upstairs and down . . ."

"Be careful, be careful," said the clerk, beginning to breathe like a Yogi; "don't talk about her any more, or I'll cry."

I LOVE YOU
I LOVE YOU
I LOVE YOU

I LOVE YOU, I LOVE YOU,
I LOVE YOU

SHE came over and into my bed and leaned her ash-blond head on my new *framboise*-colored twelve-fifty Saks-Fifth Avenue pajamas, and then in the cadences of Leslie Howard, with her eyes on my lips, in three distinct shadings, soft, softer, and the last words in an almost inaudible whispered tone, she said, "I love you, I love you, I will always love you." And she added, "I hope you will take me back to Paris when the trouble is over and when the *Normandie* is painted new again."

I said that I hoped I could soon, that I hoped all the boats would be painted new again soon, and to myself I said that I hoped also that she would be able to say, "I love you, I love you, I will always love you" exactly as she had said it, on the stage, because then she would be a great actress. But I am afraid that, instead, my daughter Barbara will be the pen pal of some future desperado, or, if we're very lucky, the chatelaine of Alcatraz or Sing Sing.

Barbara was then three and a half years old; most of her

life has been spent in Europe; she has also been in Chile, Peru, Ecuador, and Cuba. She knows the captains of at least half a dozen liners. Everywhere she has met nice people and left them nicely alone—and everywhere, with the nose of a retriever, she has found out and attached herself immediately to some socially maladjusted individual.

In Paris, Barbara formed an underworld friendship with a backstairs Villon whose name was Georges. We had two friends by that name. One was bon Georges, the other bad Georges. Bon Georges is Georges Reyer, the novelist and writer for *Paris-Soir;* he had introduced me to bad Georges, who was in the words of bon Georges, *"un chef de bande sinistre."* Bad Georges was my guide to Paris at night, and he assisted me in some reportage.

Once, after a long all-night tour, we were sitting in my room about nine o'clock when there was a knock at the door. Barbara was up and came in and said that two men were outside looking for Georges. Georges's hand closed around my wrist, and he said, "Remember, I have been with you all night." The men came in, and I told them truthfully that Georges had been with me all night.

They were surprised and said to me to be very certain of that; then they said, *"C'est une affaire extrêmement grave."* The one with the beard who said that seemed to love this phrase—he repeated it several times. They left without taking Georges with them. Georges said a prayer after they were gone and offered me back my watch, a watch which I had missed since the first day I met him. He said he had been sorry about it all along. I thanked him. Barbara said that it was *"une affaire extrêmement grave,"* and Georges said, "Ah, you are so right, most *extrêmement grave."*

I wanted at the time to get a nurse for Barbara, to take her to the park and to watch out for her. Several applicants came, but Barbara did not want a nurse. Georges, who was always with us, could be her nurse, she said. I told her that men were not nurses, but she said they were; she had seen the little daughter of an Indian maharaja who lived in the hotel go out with a nurse who was a man, wore a turban and a beard, and played with the little dark-skinned child in the Champs-Élysées. Georges said he loved no one better than Barbara, but I said no.

We walked out of the Ritz on the Rue Cambon side, up toward the Madeleine. On the right-hand side there is a toy shop. In this shop Barbara saw a small statue of Napoleon on horseback, brightly painted in the manner of a toy soldier. Immediately she wanted it.

Barbara has methods of stating a claim that put the propaganda of *Doktor* Goebbels to shame. Here is the work she did on Napoleon: "Papa promised Barbara a toy—please buy a toy for Barbara, Barbara wants a toy, a toy for Barbara, Barbara wants the little soldier on the horse, please buy the soldier—Mamma said Barbara could have a toy, please buy a toy for Barbara."

This nasal singsong text, wailed off-key like reedy, Oriental beggar music, is repeated for three hours. It is like having two peanut whistles tied to your ears; after a while one does not hear the words any more, just the music, but there is also a grip on the trousers, pushing and pulling, and tears are in readiness for the final effect.

"All right, Barbara, we'll go back and buy the little soldier if you only stop this, if you promise to be quiet."

"Don't be a fool," says Georges. "Don't be a fool and buy it. I will steal it for her."

We had arrived near the Madeleine, and I asked whether we could sit down and have a drink and an ice cream before we went back to buy the Napoleon. Bar-

bara weighed this for a moment and then agreed. Georges
said he had to go somewhere and excused himself. He was
back by the time I paid the bill, and sat down and ordered another drink. He gave the Napoleon to Barbara
under the table, and, with both hands and tilted head,
cut my protest short. "It is nothing," he said.

31

Georges was thin and small, he wore a cigarette on his right ear and a cap, his jacket was tight as a brassière and rode up over his hips when he walked. He was continually pulling it down. He looked like an advertisement for a *bal musette*. The arrangement for taking Barbara out was made at the end of a three-and-a-half-hour filibuster that went something like this: "Barbara wants to go with Georges, Papa promised that Barbara could go with Georges, Georges wants to take Barbara to the park——"

Georges reported every day, and he was an ideal nurse. He took Barbara to the Luxembourg, walked around with her while she rode the little donkeys, sailed boats for her in the Tuileries, took her to the Jardin d'Acclimatation, and out to the Restaurant Robinson in the trees.

The first time they came back from a Punch and Judy show, I was not there, and they both sat in that long corridor of the Ritz which is lined with show-cases. Georges's eyes were on the rings, bracelets, pendants, and wristwatches in the show-cases.

Olivier, the maître d'hôtel, passed and saw him, and he called the doorman and the reception clerk and asked everyone, *"Qui est ce phénomène-là?"* Somebody had seen Barbara before, so they asked her, and she said that Georges was a friend of Papa.

"And who is Papa?"

"Papa has no hair," said Barbara by way of explana-

tion, and then she added, *"C'est une affaire extrêmement grave."*

"Ah—oui, ah oui, alors," said Olivier, *"extrêmement grave."*

Even the maid was worried and said it would end very badly and I would be sorry the rest of my life for letting

Barbara go out with this creature. There is, she said, such a thing as *"le kidnap."*

The next day, after they had gone, I was a little worried. I looked down out of the window. The Place Vendôme was filled with chauffeurs and the municipal shade of green that was on its freshly painted lampposts and auto-buses. Usually buses do not run here, but the Rue Royale was being torn up to be recobbled, and the buses that usually go to the Madeleine passed in front of the hotel. A Senegalese Negro, with feet like two *pains de ménage*, climbed across the square.

On one corner stood two men, one carrying a big easy-chair, the other a bouquet of pink and white tulips stuck in mimosa. They waited for the traffic to pass; and when this got tiresome, one put down the chair and the other sat down on it and smelled his bouquet. A sailor, with some teeth missing, was making love to a girl leaning on a lamppost; a couple crossed the center of the square with three black poodles.

In front of the Palais de Justice stood a German tourist in shirt-sleeves and *Lederhosen*, held up by embroidered suspenders. He had a green hat with *Gemsbart* on it, a cigar, and a Baedeker. The greatest charm of Paris is that here in this bright light no one paid any attention to a couple with three black poodles, to the man in the easy-chair with his bouquet, or to the man in a Tirolian costume. The view from a Paris window is never monotonous.

After a while Georges and Barbara came out of the
hotel right under my window; they walked to Schiaparelli's store. Barbara stopped and looked at the stuffed white
doves that hang in it, suspended from thin wires, and
Georges lifted her little white dog Fifi so that the dog
could see them too. Then they walked on to Cartier's. I
was afraid—they had a gold-and-pearl elephant clock in
the window which Barbara wanted. I thought for a moment that she would ask Georges for it. I could just hear

her say to him, "Papa promised an elephant for Barbara, please buy the elephant for Barbara, Barbara wants an elephant——"

She did. Georges ground a few centimeters of cigarette under his heel, pulled down his jacket, looked around, and then shook his head. I looked around, too, and was greatly relieved—there were three *agents de la Sûreté*, with their eyes on Georges. Two of them followed him and Barbara down to the park. There was no need to worry—Barbara was the best-guarded child in Paris.

STAR OF HOPE

THREE infantrymen, their arms interlocked, came up the Boulevard Raspail. My friend Georges leaned over the marble-topped red table and said, "I am ashamed whenever I see such soldiers! Look at them, walking arm in arm like girls! When they are far away they look blue, then they slowly get dirty, and when they are close to you, you can observe that their uniforms never, never fit. They are like horse blankets with a bandage wrapped around the middle.

"Look at them—how they wear the cap, and the cigarette hanging out of one corner of the mouth! And the shoes! Too big! And not shined! And the uniform always dirty! The Germans are too clean, and the English walk with their hands in their pockets, but the American soldiers—that is something else. I love America!"

The three soldiers, now hanging together with their elbows around each other's necks, had turned the corner and were going down the Boulevard Montparnasse. They sang, and one looked back at the legs of a woman who was emptying a pail of water into the street.

A waiter came and spoke a few words to Georges, using his hand as a screen between his mouth and Georges's ear. Georges got up and walked to the rear of the café and spoke to a girl. She had a young, obedient face and raven hair. She gave him something, or he gave something to her. Georges sat down at the table again, and the girl passed by without stopping and went out on the sidewalk.

"I must be very careful," said Georges, and looked around. "I must be very careful. One can never tell, because if they recognize me and catch me, it is good-by. I will go to prison for long, stupid years—and in France prison is not a club like in America.

"But I don't think they will catch me. The French police are very dull. They make their round-up always at the same time, always the same police. I know them from far away. Every child knows them. It is not fun to elude them—just tiresome and a matter of watching the clock."

A stout policeman with a Hitler mustache, his cloak draped over one shoulder, the thumbs of his round hands stuck in his belt, slowly passed in front of the sidewalk café.

"Look!" said Georges. "Look at him! Look at the face!

41

You have police like that in America? I don't think so.
You have G-men, not police to laugh at!"

Georges drank some black coffee, then he turned and
watched two women who had sat down a few tables away
from ours. They were large and well dressed. One of them
talked very loudly. "My cousin Jaqueneau," she said,
"owns the property. It's an original grant from the king
of——"

"Fake!" said Georges. "Fake jewelry. Yes, the jewelry is certainly fake. I can see that from here even without glasses.

"The ring and the brooch are fake too," he added, leaning forward.

"And so are the earrings," he concluded, and turned
away.

"Of course, there are always the traveler's checks. Don't
look now, but her bag, on the chair, is open. Inside, in the
little black folder, there are the traveler's checks.

"They are a nuisance, traveler's checks. Lately they
come in very small amounts—five dollars, ten dollars, seldom higher. You have to sit up all night and practice the
signature or, what is worse, teach a girl to sign them. Then
you must run to some night-club in Montmartre, sit and
drink a while, and, when it is late enough, cash them and
get out. I prefer money, or jewels.

"Paris has changed," he sighed. "Oh, how Paris has
changed! I lie awake at night trying to think about new

ideas, but it is all for nothing, everything has been tried.

"It is almost impossible to live here any more, and I am one who is alert and willing to work hard, but—" He snapped the sentence shut, shrugged his lean shoulders, and with his hands said, "What is the use!"

"In America you have at least the hold-up to count on. But the French people, they don't believe in it, they don't believe in it at all. They don't think that the gun can be loaded! They don't believe it can be dangerous because nobody in France has ever been shot in a hold-up. You can go in, anywhere, ask for the proprietor, and when he comes, point a gun at his stomach. You know what happens? You know what he will do? He will argue with you!

"If some intelligent people would only get together

here, hold up fifty or sixty people and shoot them, then perhaps they would begin to take it seriously. But we have no co-operation here. That is why I love America.

"Of course there are other things. There is the casino. For a while I made a little money playing roulette, but I became very nervous. I placed my bets on the colors. When the color was right, I left my bet. But when I lost, I quickly snatched it back, in a split second's time. Sometimes the croupier would start a scandal, but then I would say, 'Ah, sorry, I thought I still had time.' Sometimes they made me march to the director's office, and the director tore up my card of admission and the casino telephoned to all the other casinos not to let me in. I had to change my name and get a new card. But eventually they begin to remember the face, and then the game is over.

"Once I had a little business, in the Gare St.-Lazare. It was a telephone business, and it was good as long as the calls cost one franc. I had twelve telephones in this station. I went every morning and put a little cotton in each one of them. When people want to get their money back after calling a wrong number, and move the hook up and down, the franc falls down, but it does not come out. During the afternoon hours I returned and collected, sometimes eighteen francs, sometimes twenty—not much, but it was a steady income. I wanted to include the Gare du Nord too, but just then they changed the telephones.

"In the quiet months, when there are no tourists, when

things are very bad, when I am altogether broke, then I have to work very hard to make twenty francs.

"As a last resort, I go to a rooming house, late at night. I look very respectable and serious in a dark suit, and I ask for a room with a wide bed, because it is much easier to get rid of double-size sheets. I pay for the room in advance, for one night's lodging. I notice immediately, as I walk in, whether or not there is a little carpet. If there is none, then I explain to the woman that I am a peculiar fellow and that I like a little rug in front of my bed; also that I cannot stand towels with holes or frayed edges. In the middle of the night I get up, pack the little rug, the sheets, the pillowcases, mirror, towels, and curtains in my bag, and leave quietly.

"I go directly to a place where the complete outfit is bought at the regular price of thirty francs. Deduct from that the ten francs paid in advance, and you have left twenty francs for one night's work! Oh, I am so tired of this country!"

Georges ordered another glass of coffee. The girl who had spoken to him earlier in the rear of the restaurant passed in front of the tables with a man. Georges went on: "The mentality of the French people is awful. They mistrust everybody. You could lie here in the street like a dog and they would leave you there. No one will turn a hand to help you, and if they find out that you have done something bad, then they will kick you on top of it!

"In America, in the United States, do the people there have a nice mentality and not think that everybody is a thief and a crook? Do they behave nicely? Do they give you hospitality? Do you think if I arrived there with two or more nice girls—you know, *goût américain*—that I could do a little business?

"Not on the sidewalk like here, of course. I mean a *salon*, on Fifth Avenue, with a maid in a white cap and a little apron, a few bottles of champagne, everything very nice, and the right connection with the government.

It would take a lot of money of course, the passage, the furniture, the government, and the girls.

"I could have made a good deal of money here last night," he said, "enough for all the expenses and more for a small reserve capital. Last night they sold sixteen thousand francs' worth of heroin, right here.

"Turn around and look at the bar. Over the bar you see some light fixtures, glass tubes with light in them, neon lights. One of the tubes you see is without light. That is where they keep it, inside the tube. The maître d'hôtel here is in this business also.

"I don't like to deal in it regularly. It's too dangerous.

But once in a while, for a good supper, a nice present for someone, for a vacation in Deauville, or to help out a friend—then it's all right.

"The price changes. Now we sell it to the girls on the street for fifty francs the gram. They sell it again for perhaps seventy-five.

"The profit is in the Americans. They pay more—at least a hundred and fifty francs—and for that they get just a little bit of heroin. We mix it for them—seventy-five percent bicarbonate of soda and twenty-five percent heroin.

"They love it, but they are good for only one sale. The next day they go to Versailles. But no matter what price you ask, *O.K., Georgie,* they say, and pay. Oh, I love America!"

PALE HANDS

« 4 »

PALE HANDS

ON ONE of the bright days of the spring of 1940, when the Maginot Line still held, Hippolyte De Glenzer gazed up into the untroubled Paris sky. His face, which normally looked as if it just had been slapped, looked less so for a little while as he calculated the neat profits from two small old masters that had been sold for him in New York and thought of the sum that had been deposited for him in a New York bank. The high heels on which he walked, attached to patent-leather pumps (he was only five feet three without them), clattered down the Rue des Gobelins, and he whistled and turned over in his mind the pleasant idea of running out on the misery that no one here saw coming. Although his right hand was bandaged, he rubbed both hands together gently. At the end of the street he stood still for a moment and then, with his bandaged hand, waved for a taxi and got in it. He said good-by to everything as he looked out of the window of the moving cab; he smiled indulgently at a poster that advertised armament bonds and, as he passed a *succursale* of the Crédit Lyonnais, he closed his eyes and spelled to himself

51

the name of the New York bank where his money was secure and waiting.

He got out of the taxi at the Café du Dôme and sat down at a sidewalk table to wait for his friend Georges. Georges was his sometime secretary, valet, friend, chauffeur, and mechanic. M. De Glenzer had with him a small green envelope with some money in it for Georges—a bonus on a transaction a few months old. From his corner table, De Glenzer looked up and down the Boulevards Raspail and Montparnasse, but did not see Georges. At the table next to him someone said that Hitler was only bluffing, that the war was a fake.

Just before the trouble began, a few weeks before the German-French frontier was closed, Georges had driven De Glenzer across the border in an open car into whose double canvas top two van Goghs, a Hieronymus Bosch, and three Holbeins had been sewn. They had got into France a few hours ahead of the agents of the *Kulturministerium* and the Gestapo, who had caught the poor fellow who had sold them the paintings. Everything went quietly, professionally, without excitement or trouble until they had safely passed the border; then Georges drove like a madman, and at Nancy, the first place they stopped on the way to Paris, he poured drink after drink into himself to celebrate the deed, and then he said to De Glenzer, "Ah! I like you. I like you very much," and slapped him between the shoulders. De Glenzer swayed on his bar stool, coughed,

and fell, and a brandy glass broke in his hand and almost severed his thumb. He had had the cut attended to immediately, but the wound had become infected, and in Paris he had had to go to a hospital; now it was properly sewed up with six stitches, and healing.

De Glenzer looked at the restaurant's clock for the seventh time; he had waited for half an hour. He decided to go, but just as he was paying his bill, Georges arrived. He had come from around the corner, where the Cinéma Raspail was, had walked from there to the newspaper kiosk, proceeded to the flower wagon, and quickly run into the

Dôme. He had entered it through the side door where the cigarette stand is, from there had crossed through the bar, and had surprised De Glenzer, who was looking into the street, expecting him to come from there.

De Glenzer offered his unbandaged hand and then gave Georges the green envelope. Georges counted the contents and said that the sum was acceptable, in fact most generous, and while he put the money in a black wallet and stowed the wallet away in his inside coat pocket, De Glenzer informed him that he hoped to go to America.

"You are right. Good God, here it's no longer fun! It's misery; it's a rotten life. If I could only get out of here, too! *La Belle France*—bah!" said Georges. "I would love to go with you to America. I think I would like it there.

A nice woman, you know—not poor. She does not have to be young, not very young, and she does not need to own a Château de Sans-Souci. What I want is comfort. I'm a homebody. I love a nice home, furniture. I would do the marketing myself. I would attend to her, make her happy. I know how to do this. Do you know anyone like that in America? Do they understand an arrangement like that?" He looked down at his hands, which were gloved.

"I love soft gloves," he went on. "Yellow gloves." He took them off and De Glenzer saw that his hands were pale.

He had never seen Georges's hands before. "It is a habit with me. I seldom work without gloves. One leaves no fingerprints that way. I am so used to them that my hands feel uncomfortable when I have no gloves on them. It's like dreaming you are without your trousers in a large room filled with people. I even wore them when I sat in front of the hotel in Noirmoutier, and everyone took me for an English lord. I should have stayed there longer. It is dangerous for me here; the police are still on the alert. It was much nicer in Noirmoutier—the sand, the sun, and only one policeman, an idiot. That is why I would like to be in America, away from the police—start a new life. I think I have come back too soon. It is not safe for me here."

Georges's sharp face was sunburned to a dark-brown olive shade; only his hands were pale. He told De Glenzer that he had got tanned hiding out on the Ile de Noirmoutier. He had sat day after day on a bench in back of the orphan asylum without a hat; his had been blown into the water crossing over to the island. He had kept his hands in his pockets or in his gloves.

Georges looked up and down the legs of a young woman who passed the tables of the Café du Dôme and then said, "What were we talking about? Oh, yes, we were talking about the police. I have come back too soon. I sense this. I get a feeling somewhere here in back of my head, between the ears; my collar gets warm and then hot, and I know there is danger. I feel this now. I know I must make myself scarce for a while longer. I should have stayed another month—it was nice in Noirmoutier. I will have to make another trip. I must go away again. I think I will go to Basle; I have an aunt there. I know Basle well—a lovely city. Have you ever been in Basle? There, to the right—don't look now. Two tables away from us, the man who pretends to read the paper, the one with a copy of *Paris-Soir* in his paws—look at him."

De Glenzer looked.

"I think I am speaking the truth," Georges went on, "when I say that only an agent of the police can have a physiognomy so blank, so gross, so stupid. Let's go. Follow me, this way."

Georges went ahead, turned, and scurried down the circular stairway inside the Café du Dôme, where the men's washroom is. Just before one goes into the washroom there is another door. This door Georges opened. They went through it to the kitchen and into the back street. Georges threw the butt of his cigarette away and pressed against the houses. He moved so fast that De Glenzer had to run and was out of breath when they came to the end of the street. He jumped after Georges to the rear platform of a passing bus. Georges bought the tickets, folded them, and stuck them under a wedding ring which he wore on the index finger of his pale left hand.

"My gloves," Georges said, "I forgot my gloves!" He

shrugged his shoulders and put his hands in his pockets. "I must go tonight," he said. "I will find out when a train leaves. I have to make some arrangements before I go. I have a good friend who is the headwaiter at the Café des Deux Magots. You know the place. I must speak to him. He is my banker and does some business for me. Here we are," he said, and jumped off when the bus turned the corner facing the Deux Magots.

They sat down at a small table in front of the café. In the square there was a great commotion—a taxi had rammed a baker's delivery tricycle, and a bus, trying to avoid a further collision, had swerved, mounted the sidewalk, and crashed through the iron gate of the little park next to the Church of St. Germain des Prés. Three gendarmes were busy restraining the various characters in the drama.

Each of the gendarmes, his short blue cape thrown back over both shoulders, gestured with a pencil stub with which he wanted to write a report of the accident in his notebook. They waved these notebooks while the drivers of the vehicles shouted at each other, *"Andouille!" "Tête de lard!" "Chauffeur du dimanche!" "Tordu!"*

A trembling little man sat on the steps of the rectory holding a handkerchief to his face; the *curé*'s housekeeper brought him a glass of water and helped him inside. The headwaiter friend of Georges's explained that the little man had just missed being crushed against the iron gate

when the bus mounted the sidewalk, and had nearly collapsed from fright.

The headwaiter then shouted for his waiters. They were all in the street, waving their napkins and giving eye-witness accounts of the accident. One of them held up the front wheel of the tricycle, which was in the shape of a figure eight, and pointed at the driver of the taxi. The headwaiter went out into the square and chased them all back to the café.

Unconcerned with all this excitement, a Hindu passed through the crowd with dignity. He walked very erect, in native garb, and clinging to him, hobbling along noiselessly on feet stuck into small high-heeled shoes, was a short, dark, East Indian woman. The Hindu and his companion headed for the jewelry shop at the left of the café.

Georges looked after them and remarked how wonderful it was that in Paris one could dress up in any fashion one pleased and no one bothered about it. "Yes, yes," said Georges. "It is very nice, very, very nice." His eyes roved over every visible part of the streets, the square, in and out of the restaurant. His eyes were like gulls that ride the air; they never rested.

A little while after the Hindu and the little woman had gone into the jewelry shop, they came out. The woman trotted along, holding onto the Hindu's robe, and she tinkled now.

"I don't believe it," said Georges. "Look!" He pointed at the woman's feet. De Glenzer looked down and saw that she wore bracelets on her right ankle, six golden bracelets which the Hindu must have just bought for her. They tinkled as she walked.

The Hindu sat down at a table in back of De Glenzer and Georges and called for a waiter by clapping his hands. He wanted to order something. He repeated the order three times, but the waiter shrugged his shoulders. He could not seem to understand the Hindu. The waiter went to get the headwaiter. The Hindu repeated his order with gestures, but the headwaiter did not understand him either. Georges leaned back and listened, then said to De Glenzer, "I believe this gentleman is trying to speak English." He listened again and then said, "I believe this gentleman cannot speak French. It sounds like some kind of English to me. Yes, he is trying to speak English; it's very bad English, but I think I know what he wants. I think he wants a gin-and-tonic for himself and a chocolate-and-vanilla ice for the lady, and some pastry." Georges then smiled and turned to the Hindu and said, "Excuse me. My name is Georges Duval. Allow me to order for you." He called the headwaiter and told him what they wanted. The Hindu was very grateful. He rose and crossed his arms over his chest, saying, "Thank you, thank you, thank you very much." Bowing solemnly, he sat down.

Georges then spoke to his headwaiter friend and gave him a small package. He had hardly done this when he took De Glenzer's arm and said, "I must go now. I must leave you immediately. But you will hear from me. I will write you a note. I am taking the train for Basle tonight." He looked out into the square while he talked, and de Glenzer saw that the man who had sat close to their table at the Dôme reading *Paris-Soir* now talked to one of the gendarmes, who was writing in his notebook. Then Georges was gone.

There was a knock at De Glenzer's door late that night.

Georges came in; he was cold and he had no hat. "I can't go home for anything," he said. "They are there already."

De Glenzer asked him whether he wanted more money, but Georges said he had enough. He pulled out his wallet and showed De Glenzer two of the four five-hundred-franc Swiss banknotes which De Glenzer had given him that afternoon, and some change; he also had his ticket to Basle. He had given the rest to the headwaiter to keep for him.

He needed clothes; he wanted to borrow a coat and a hat. There were a bowler and a raincoat in the closet of the room and he took them, then said, "Gloves. Quickly, gloves. I almost forgot the gloves. I am certain that by now my *signalement* is broadcast—pale hands, dark complexion. I must have gloves." De Glenzer had several pairs of new English gloves; he picked out a yellow pair and gave them to Georges. Georges shook hands and said, while putting on the gloves, that his friend would hear from him soon. He waved good-by with a yellow-gloved hand and was gone. He waved with his left hand. Georges was left-handed.

Some ten days later De Glenzer sat, as he did every day at around five, at the leftmost marble-topped table in front of the Café des Deux Magots, and next to his table sat the man with the physiognomy of the *agents de la Sûreté*.

He was almost always there. He had started a nodding acquaintance, and De Glenzer had always nodded back to him, but they never spoke. The *agent* read, as usual, his copy of *Paris-Soir* and then sat for a while, finishing a cigar. He put the paper down, yawned several times, and wearily looked for the waiter. The waiter came and counted the saucers; the man paid, got up, and went away, leaving his paper on the chair. De Glenzer picked it up and started to read it. It was folded down the middle of the second page, and at the top of the page

I LOVE YOU, I LOVE YOU, I LOVE YOU

was the report of a murder. The headlines told the story:

TRAGIC NIGHT ON THE
BOULEVARD MAGENTA

AFTER HAVING KILLED HIS AUNT,
A YOUNG HAIRDRESSER
DISAPPEARS

"SHE DID NOT WANT TO FOLLOW ME TO
AFRICA," SAYS THE MURDERER

Right under this was another item of crime, with headlines in large type:

NOTHING IN HIS HANDS
BUT THE BANKNOTES
IN HIS POCKET

A CROOK DISGUISED AS A HINDU
MAKES DISAPPEAR $2,300
FROM A BANK TELLER

The story had come by telephone from the paper's special envoy in Basle. Translated, it read as follows:

Yesterday afternoon there presented himself at the window of a large bank in Basle a young man of exotic allure, his hair in a turban, his hands in bright-lemon-yellow gloves, and speaking with a frightful English jargon.

From his gestures and words, the clerk deduced that he wanted to change a Swiss banknote of five hundred francs against dollars. The cashier brought out of his strongbox a little package of American banknotes and showed them to the Hindu. That one took them an instant into his hands to examine them from nearby, but he gave them back immediately to the cashier, not without manifesting his most lively disappointment for having been misunderstood. The cashier excused himself and the difficult palaver began again. After a new and very expressive pantomime, the man in the turban succeeded finally in making himself understood—it was not at all dollars that he desired to receive but pounds sterling. The cashier, now much relieved, hastened to change the five hundred Swiss francs of the Hindu against English bills.

Our Hindu bowed solemnly, the arms crossed on his breast, before the cashier who had served him so well, and left the bank with measured step.

It was only in the evening, after the closing of the door, that our cashier, while verifying his cash, established, not without bitterness, that he lacked thirty-five bills of various denominations, which represented in total the *coquette* sum of 130,000 francs.

The Hindu, in examining the package of American banknotes, had, it appears, made the thirty-five bills disappear. The cashier observed that the Hindu was lefthanded.

It is now the turn of the police of Basle to search for a young man with dark *teint*, lemon-yellow gloves, the hair dressed in a turban, and to decide whether he is really a Hindu or quite simply a professional crook disguised as a man of that race.

De Glenzer left Paris soon after. He had not heard from Georges. He worried about him and often thought of him, and consoled himself with the knowledge that in times of turmoil such characters as Georges usually fare well. De Glenzer arrived in New York with trunk and baggage on the *Excambion* and took up residence in a smart and quiet hotel between Park and Lexington Avenues, in the Fifties. He felt at home there; it had the smells and sounds of the Meurice or the Plaza-Athénée. In the elevators, in the corridors and lobbies, English was rarely spoken, French and German predominated, and there was some Hungarian, Polish, and Rumanian; it sounded like Maxim's at noon and, particularly at 5 p.m., it was crowded with overperfumed women, pomaded men, and monocles.

On a Friday afternoon, about a month after he had arrived in New York, De Glenzer called for the manager of the hotel. He wanted to give a party and wondered whether, instead of paying for a private dining room, he could use the sitting room of his suite. He wanted to have the grand piano moved out and a small one put in. On the grand piano stood a row of pictures of wonderful girls. He had obtained these from a refugee fashion photographer who also promised to bring some of the girls themselves to the party. When the manager, Mr. Kalbfuss, came in, De Glenzer was busy opening a bottle of Chilean champagne. It had been recommended to him by a South American diplomat; it was supposed to be excellent and cheap.

Mr. Kalbfuss looked around the room, at the piano, at the beautiful girls in silver frames, and said, "Certainly, certainly. Of course, of course, M. De Glenzer. With pleasure."

De Glenzer thanked the manager and offered him a glass of the greenish champagne. He asked for his frank opinion about the wine. The manager rolled the champagne on his tongue and said he thought it was so-so, just so-so; nothing for a dinner but all right for champagne cocktails, with a napkin wrapped around the bottle. He asked whether he could sit down for a minute. "No one can find me here," he said. "I'll get a moment's rest."

De Glenzer poured him another glass of the champagne and said how very nice it was of him, the manager, to have the piano moved out. "Bah!" said Mr. Kalbfuss. "That is nothing, nothing at all, no trouble. You should know some of the things one has to do in this business, M. De Glenzer," he said slowly, and wagged a finger. "You have no idea what we have to go through sometimes. It is unthinkable. There is not even a dream like it. You should thank God, M. De Glenzer, that you are an art dealer and not a hotel man. Yes, you have really to thank God for that every day."

M. De Glenzer clucked sympathetically and started to take the girls off the piano.

"As for pianos, hear what happened to me two days ago, M. De Glenzer," said the manager. "You would not believe such a thing could happen. I don't know how I could have fallen for it. It's the oldest trick in the business, and it wouldn't have happened to me if he had not asked me to break down a wall. A man comes in here; he looks about thirty, a refugee. He had lunch in the restaurant with an elderly woman, very well dressed—fox scarf, dog, diamonds. First they did not like the table they got, and after they were seated they looked at the menu and complained about our assortment of dishes. The man continually snapped his fingers at the waiter; the best was not good enough. They ordered a quart of Krug '28. Half of the food they sent back to the kitchen, saying that this and that was wrong with it. Then they called the headwaiter and complained about the service, and at the end the man signed the bill. He left a very poor tip, just like a really rich man. Then he sent for me.

"He said he wanted to look at some rooms. I took him upstairs myself, and showed him 98, the suite right above this one. He remarked that he liked the hotel—the furniture and everything was all right. The only thing he objected to was the sitting room—it was too small. He tapped on the wall with his cane and asked what was next door, so I showed him 99, the adjoining suite; he wanted to rent the two suites, he said, and break the wall through. He said he needed the space so that he could have his two grand pianos in this room, one facing this way and the other that way. He tapped some more on the wall and I telephoned for the engineer.

"The engineer came up and said yes, it could be done. We telephoned the renting agents, who have the final say about this, and they said that it was all right to knock down the wall.

"The man said to send a truck for his trunks and gave one of the best hotels in the city as his address. So just to play safe, just as a matter of routine, you know, I had someone call up, and they said yes, he's registered there and he's all right.

"On the way down he asked me to cash a check; he needed a hundred and twenty-five dollars. Here is the check. It is a false signature. He had given me the name of someone he knew was staying at that other hotel.

"The police were here. They asked me what he looks like. The only thing I remember about him is that he's about five feet six and he wore yellow gloves, and he wrote out the check with his left hand."

Hippolyte De Glenzer looked up as if far away he heard

a familiar tune being played. The manager said, "I never would have fallen for it if he hadn't asked me to break through the wall. Nobody ever asked for that before."

De Glenzer went to the Colony for lunch to discuss terms for a Gauguin sketch. He looked through the crowd assembled at the good and bad tables as he sat down to wait for his client. Time and again, he had a feeling that Georges might be somewhere in the room, but he did not see him. A few nights later he thought he saw Georges jump out of a cab as he crossed Madison Avenue after dining at Voisin's. He knew Georges's motions well, but the man was too far away for him to be sure. Whoever he was, he disappeared through the door of a night club. A woman was with him. In silhouette they looked like Jimmy Walker and Louella Parsons.

De Glenzer followed them into the night club and was seated. The man who looked like Georges was across the room on a banquette near the circular bar. His head was turned away, for he was talking to his companion, a white-haired *grande dame*, with face and arms like asbestos, whose head was constantly in motion. The body, in black velvet, sat straight up, the neck was wrapped in a choker of diamonds. The occupants of the table suggested Goya, the Gestapo, the fall of France, the foyer of the Meurice, an altar in a Spanish church, a sepulcher with the bejeweled relics of an old saint. The man turned and looked at de Glenzer. He recognized his friend. He sent a small, sad smile across to De Glenzer and raised his hand—the left one. It was as pale as the woman's throat. De Glenzer waved back to Georges with his own right, the one with the cut and the six stitches.

WATCH THE BIRDIE

5

WATCH THE BIRDIE

D<small>URING</small> that soft, green, May-wine-and-guitar-music period when Mozart, von Hofmannsthal, and Salzburg were the fashion and Queen Marie of Rumania came to the Passion Play at Oberammergau in a Schiaparelli dirndl, the young Polish photographer Zygmunt Pisik arrived in Salzburg, let his hair grow long over his ears, and changed his name to Johann von Schönberg.

He photographed everything in Salzburg, and he loved an ample, pink woman who was like a peasant commode with wide drawers that were filled with kindness, honesty, and submission—the cold Mamsell of the Hotel zum Frommen Brunnen. She was called the cold Mamsell because she supervised the buffet where salami, ham, and other cold delicatessen were served. She, too, wore a dirndl. Her hair was braided. She walked and stood in solid footgear. With a clop, clop, clop, gallop, she came out every evening and met Johann von Schönberg at a certain bench under a linden tree, and there was always a roll in her handbag, buttered and weighed down with a considerable slice of tender ham. "Here, darling," she handed him the roll and gave him a kiss that was like the butter on the roll.

After one Salzburg season von Schönberg went to Berlin and worked for *Die Dame*, a German imitation of *Vogue*. He also contributed photographs to other magazines, and his art flourished when he began to photograph the nude.

The pictures he took of unclad young women in the snow, on skis, of two of them playing with a pushball, of one kneeling in dejection, of one with eyes half closed under a thin black veil, of one on a polar-bear rug and labeled "Baroness X," found their way through the editorial room to the press with miraculous ease.

Von Schönberg was known among his colleagues as the worm photographer. He took most of his pictures lying flat on his stomach, with the camera tilted up. Girls photographed from that angle became his trademark. It was inevitable that such talent should take him to Paris. He wrapped up the polar-bear rug, packed in a leisurely fashion, and was boarding the train at the moment when an agent of the Goebbels Ministry appeared at *Die Dame* to request a list of the personnel. Schönberg was a certified Aryan with all his grandparents in order, but he disliked Nazis and on several occasions had said so, quite loudly. He was, besides, a Pole, with burnt-sienna skin and thick, shiny black hair, and there were a good many golden-haired and blue-eyed youths around who also could take pictures.

He arrived in Paris in German pants that rode high

over his shoes. His hat suggested an excursion into the Black Forest and his shirt choked him.

He found a girl to pose for him and to clean his studio. Her name was Denise and she wore colored ribbons in her hair and she was always cold. They went out to eat together and she sat with a heavy sweater on, listening to him across one of the tables of the Restaurant Cécile, where the *choucroute à l'ancienne*, with napkin and bread and butter included, was seven francs. She didn't mind his German clothes. She loved him as he was.

His life changed when he met Roxanne Colombo and photographed her glossy Italian beauty backstage at the Bal Tabarin. She had him change his name to Henri de Beaumont. She saw to it that his hair was cut. He became thinner. He walked with elegance. Roxanne went with him to the tailor and the shoemaker. A thin mustache bloomed under his nose. Denise disappeared from his life.

Besides photographing pretty women, de Beaumont invented an editorial game which consisted of printing, side by side, pictures that complemented each other. There would be, for example, on the left-hand page a photograph of an old sea lion who looked like an ancient mariner, and on the opposite page a photograph of an ancient mariner who looked like an old sea lion. In his new habitat, a studio on the fifth floor of a modern building near the Observatoire, he pasted up a layout in which a pig and Julius Streicher were juxtaposed.

De Beaumont got several assignments after the layout appeared, together with a group of his nudes, in a French imitation of *Vogue*. He was sent to take photographs of a circus party given by Lady Mendl. He took snaps at Auteuil and at the various fêtes that were arranged by the Syndicat d'Initiative of the City of Paris, and in between these routine jobs he lay on his stomach in the sands of Le Touquet and Deauville and in the early, unpoliced morning mists of the Bois de Boulogne. He moved to

Clichy, and went to the Tabarin every evening in a midnight-blue dinner jacket with a blood-red carnation in his lapel. The maître d'hôtel sat him at a table while he waited for Roxanne to sing the quatrain that ended the show:

> *Princesses, duchesses, et marquises,*
> *Féerie lumière, oubli décor,*
> *Plus de cafard, à bas la crise;*
> *On peut rire de tout encore.*

79

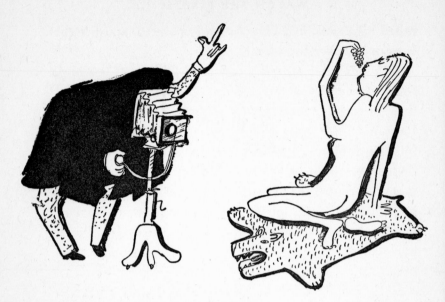

Roxanne appeared in the nude on one negative after another until there were stacks of them. She did her turn on the polar-bear rug and she was shown holding up a balloon. She was the veiled nymph in the Bois and also was photographed with her clothes on. A boy who did de Beaumont's errands and helped him in the darkroom sometimes was worked into the compositions, the most successful of which showed the Left Bank arch of the Pont Royal. Roxanne, in a shabby coat, leaned on a lamppost and the apprentice leaned on her. De Beaumont screwed the lens out of focus to obtain the mood of waterfront and despair. He called it *Sous les Ponts de Paris*, and it won the first prize at an exhibition and made him famous. He raised his prices, had his sofa newly covered, and bought Roxanne a silver-fox jacket.

Into this idyll came a fashion model from Cleveland, Ohio, whom everyone greeted with "*Allo*, Toots." She had been recruited, together with six other girls, to pose in Paris when the great French couturiers had their shows for American buyers. The young women lived together in three rooms at an eminently respectable *pension de famille* in the environs of the Eiffel Tower. Toots had taken French in high school and did her best to converse in that language, although most of the people she found herself with were polyglots, like de Beaumont, and spoke some English.

Backgrounds against which to photograph Toots immediately suggested themselves to de Beaumont—the great stairway at Versailles, the Madeleine, the fountains on the Place de la Concorde, marble horses, onyx columns, silvery trees. He looked at her professionally, optically, through a square made of his two hands, studying all her possibilities.

He stopped taking pictures of Roxanne, indeed forgot about her entirely, and lay on the grass in the Tuileries and on the pavement of the Champs-Élysées and looked up at Toots in sports clothes leaning on Daimler cabriolets, sitting at sidewalk tables. After a week the lines of her body were as familiar to him as those of the Arc de Triomphe.

On a lovely morning in May, after photographing Toots in a governess cart in the Bois, de Beaumont suggested that she come to his studio that afternoon. He gave himself time to prepare lights, he sent the apprentice away, and then he called for her in his Citroën. When they got to the studio he opened a bottle of Sauternes and arranged some blue grapes on a plate. He asked her not to eat the grapes until he was through taking pictures. He brought out a large portfolio and from it spilled an assortment of fashion shots, the best of his life's work. He also casually drew from his files a picture of a classic Greek statue. He said that he would like to use that in a magazine layout on the left-hand page and opposite, in the same pose, Toots. He said that up to now he had not found anyone worthy of that arrangement.

"*Je n'aime pas de poser dans le nude,*" said Toots.

"What are you—Snow White or something?" said de Beaumont. "What is the matter with you? Look, darling, it is only for the pleasure of the eye. There is a lot of precedent. Here, in this *dossier*——"

Toots shook her head.

"What an extraordinary child!" said de Beaumont. He put his face close to hers. "We still can do it. We will do it like the Venus de Milo—half nude, dressed from the waist down."

"I told you, *je n'aime pas du tout—du tout—de poser* that way. *C'est tout,*" she said.

While Toots straightened herself out and arranged her hair, de Beaumont poured out two glasses of the wine. He sat silent, with clouded eyes; then he said, "I wish you wouldn't be such a silly child. This has never happened to me before. This is not what you think it is. You must imagine that I am like a doctor——"

"Ha-ha," said Toots, and then, "What are you looking so sad for?"

"Oh, nothing," said de Beaumont.

"All right," she said, "I'll let you take one."

De Beaumont fished around the back of her dress until he found the locket of the zipper, but Toots shook herself and said that she'd rather do it herself. She undid the back and the tight sleeves of the black blouse and slipped it over her head. De Beaumont ran into his darkroom to get his plates. He whistled in there and knocked about and said to himself, "God, what a sweet business!" When he came out, Toots was standing in the middle of the room fully dressed. She had her hat on and she was pulling on a glove. De Beaumont made a mental note never to leave a model alone again.

"Does this furniture belong to you?" asked Toots.

"No," he said. "It goes with the apartment. Only the sofa there belongs to me. It's French Provincial. Do you like it?"

"*Ah, oui!* I had a grandmother on my mother's side who was French."

"I'm hungry," de Beaumont said.

They let themselves down in the automatic elevator.

"*Après vous*," said de Beaumont, and held open the outside door. He had never been that gallant to the others.

They drove to one of the large *brasseries* along the

Champs-Élysées, went down to the basement, and sat in a corner.

"We must speak French," Toots said while he studied the menu. "I, *moi*"—pointing at herself—"*je aime beaucoup le théâtre. Vous savez?* Sarah Bernhardt, Sacha Guitry, *la Comédie-Française. Tous les soirs*, when I can, *quand je peux*, I go to the theater, you understand. I, *moi, je veux être grande artiste—du théâtre*, or moving picture——"

"*Ça c'est très intéressant*," said de Beaumont.

She suggested that they go to the theater together, to see a performance of *Oscar Wilde* in English. "*Vous allez apprendre* English," Toots said, "and I will improve my French by translating the hard parts for you." A tight squeeze of his arm sealed this *entente cordiale*, and de Beaumont said to himself, "Time. Patience. Perhaps the next time, if I don't go out of the room. Perhaps then."

He drove her to a little theater he had never heard of. It turned out to be only one street away from the Bal Tabarin. De Beaumont bought two tickets in an upstairs loge. The curtain was painted to resemble a tapestry. It went up on a set showing the terrace of a hotel in Algiers —two broken-down wicker chairs, a tabouret on which stood an ashtray advertising the Galeries Lafayette, and a potted palm.

Lord Alfred Douglas, in a platinum-blond wig, his thin-fingered hands hanging on one hip, danced toward the place from which Oscar was to make his entrance. Toots started to translate the dialogue.

After the second act she sighed. "I have learned so much," she said. "*Avez vous remarqué le* business *avec les gloves?*"

She had tears in her eyes when the final curtain came down. She shouted "Bravo!" and applauded to six curtain calls. They stopped in a bar for a drink, and afterward de Beaumont said good night to her on the steps of the *pension de famille* near the Eiffel Tower.

For the next two weeks he did fashion shots of Toots during the day and in the evenings they met, ate, and ended up in that little island of people who huddled together in the emptiness of the Odéon Theatre and sat through dreary performances of Racine and Molière. Neither the statue of the Venus de Milo nor the polar-bear rug was brought up again.

In the summer of 1939, when the political horizon grew dark with storm clouds, Toots took the S.S. *Manhattan* back to America. De Beaumont drove her down to Boulogne-sur-Mer and waved good-by from the pier. Then he turned his Citroën around and went back to Paris. Toward midnight he was in the neighborhood of the Tabarin. He dropped in. Roxanne was still singing the same quatrain:

Princesses, duchesses, et marquises . . .

The next spring, a few weeks before the invasion of the Low Countries, de Beaumont aroused himself sufficiently from the melancholia which the American girl had imposed on him to do a montage of Winston Churchill and a bulldog. This was an instant and international success.

87

A New York magazine cabled for de Beaumont, and again, just in time, he packed and left.

His table companions aboard the ship on which he left Boulogne-sur-Mer were two Poles. One was an author's agent, Sylvan Pogoda, who had just sold the American motion-picture rights of a play and two novels. He had once spent two years in America and was returning there now for the filming of a new story. The other was the son of a painter, who was taking his father's work across. He had also been to America before. The three agreed on the character of American women.

"You will rarely see a woman in America who is bad-looking," said Pogoda. "Some of them are ravishingly beautiful. They call them long-stemmed American Beauties, and, you know, they are. The long legs, the beautiful, slim long legs. They talk with them."

"I know," said de Beaumont. "I have had experience with them."

"But it is all a *trompe-l'œil* proposition," said Pogoda. "They are wonderful to look at and they have the soul of a tennis player, or a cash register. You could cry blood over the beauty of their eyes and hair and faces, but it is all false. They do not love the dog, neither the grandfather, neither the child, least of all the husband—not even the lover. The climate also is abominable."

Day after day, usually when they walked the deck after meals, the three men continued to discuss in bad French the unalluring prospects of life in the United States.

"Where does one eat in New York?" de Beaumont asked the day before they landed.

"Ah, that too is hopeless," the others said.

"There are good restaurants in New York," Pogoda explained. "But you must be a millionaire, an American millionaire, to go there. They are out of the question for people like you and me. If you are lucky, after a while, when you meet a friend, he may take you to his *bistro*. They are hidden away in side streets, or on the avenues where the high trains run, upstairs in apartments that are fixed up as small restaurants."

"My contract runs for a year," de Beaumont said. "I will live in a cheap little room and eat in the *bistro*. I will not buy a hat, a shirt, shoes, or clothes. I will save every penny and hurry back to France."

The editor of the American publication was delighted with the fearless approaches of his new photographer. He found that the girls in college clothes taken on the lids of sandboxes along Fifth Avenue, straddling the stairs at Vassar, or the bulwarks surrounding the base of the Statue of Liberty, had great appeal for his readers. At the end of a year, de Beaumont's contract with the American publication was renewed and his visa extended.

One day he met the agent, Pogoda, who also had managed to stay in America, in the office of a publisher who wanted to bring out a photographic manual for which he,

de Beaumont, was to supply the material. Pogoda and de Beaumont went to lunch together at an expensive restaurant in the Fifties. As they followed the headwaiter, Pogoda waved to a girl in a large felt hat and said, "*Allo,* Toots."

"It's Toots!" cried de Beaumont. "I know Toots."

They went over to her table. Toots introduced de Beaumont to the man lunching with her. His name was Horace. He was a dramatic critic. Horace seemed to know Pogoda. He nodded briefly and then studied the color of his beer while the others talked with Toots. She had just returned from Hollywood, she said, and was about to start rehearsals in a play Horace had picked for her.

"I didn't know you knew her," de Beaumont said when he and Pogoda were seated at their own table. "I knew

her in Paris a couple of years ago. I didn't know she was
in Hollywood."

"Oh, she's been out there two years. Her name is now
Sandra Watteau. I went out there with her," said Pogoda.
"It's a funny story."

As they sat down they waved once more to Toots, and she waved back.

"Ah, she's lovely," said Pogoda, with his finger pointing at the oysters-and-hors-d'œuvres part of the menu. To the waiter he said, "*Donnez-moi des* bluepoints. You know, I love oysters now. I used to detest them. It's a matter of getting over the first plate. Bluepoints and *stchi à la russe*."

"And for me, some *escargots* to start with," said de Beaumont.

"But coming back to Toots. Ah, what a darling! What a body!"

While Pogoda ate the oysters, he gave a short account of a very satisfactory stretch of life with Toots.

"*Entendez*," he said. "I worked on her with flowers, bonbons, tickets, and restaurants," he said. "Absolutely nothing happens. Kiss. Good night. Thank you for a lovely time. Good-by. I went almost crazy. Do you know where their weakness lies, Henri? They are sentimental. They are sentimental, like dogs. I will explain to you—where were we? Oh, yes. I tried everything. I tried to make her jealous. I keep away. I come back. Nothing happens. So one day I met her here in this restaurant. She was with that same fellow. I tell her that I am flying to Hollywood on the eleven-o'clock plane the next day to see about the filming of *Le Moulin de la Galette*. 'I'll see you there,'

92

she says. 'I'm taking the train for Hollywood myself tomorrow. I'm going out for a part in a picture.' I said to
her, 'Oh, I can't take the plane if you go by train. Never.
I will go by train also.' 'All right,' she said. And I thought
perhaps on a train it will be easier. You know how easy
and relaxed women are on shipboard.

"She told me what train she was taking. I wanted to
engage a compartment, but it was fifty-four eighty-five
for the compartment and the fare was ninety-one fifty.
So I thought, one always can make arrangements with the
conductor. I was glad I didn't get the compartment when
I arrived at the train. Who is there? Horace. I thought
that he had come to say good-by, but he stayed. He had a
compartment for two, and when she came she put her
things in with his. . . . The soup is for me," Pogoda said
to the waiter, and then he continued. "I thought it was
again all for nothing, but then something *épatant* happened, something glorious. Horace got off to go to a place
called Central City. That is where they hold an annual
festival, a sort of cowboy celebration. Ah, Toots is on the
train alone. She had the compartment all the way to Los
Angeles. It happened in Salt Lake City. I will always love
that name, SALT–LAKE–CITY. It was morning, and
while the train stopped in the station, Toots went out to
walk up and down, and she bought a paper. All at once
she came running back to the car. She held up the front

page for me to look at, and through the window I read: PLANE CRASHES WEST OF ALBUQUERQUE. ALL ABOARD DEAD.

" 'I am so glad,' she said, as she climbed aboard. I didn't understand right away what she meant, but when the train was under way again, while we stood on one of those drafty passages between our car and the diner, wobbling in that canvas tunnel that looks like the inside of a concertina, she embraced and kissed me, and she said, 'The plane that crashed was most probably the plane you would have been on if I'd let you go, darling.'

"I put my things in with hers all the way to Hollywood, from Salt Lake City on, *cher ami*, it was as easy—" he fiddled about in the air with his soupspoon, searching for the proper words—"it was as easy as putting a letter through the mail."

BRIDE OF BERCHTESGADEN

6

BRIDE OF BERCHTESGADEN

At every hotel and inn we stopped at that summer in
Bavaria we were put into the bridal suite, because I always wrote on the register, "Bemelmans and Bride." It
was good for a laugh; Bride was an old mountain guide
and he would come into the place after I had registered,
carrying our baggage and followed by his two dogs.

Bride had a carrot-red beard, wore buckskin breeches
and hobnailed boots, and carried a guitar under his arm
when he wasn't climbing mountains. He looked like a
souvenir-postcard picture of a Tirolian. He was a famous
guide and usually hung around the crags of the Ortler,
Grossglockner, and Watzmann Mountains. He was my
friend, and one of God's outstanding creatures. The last
time I was with him we climbed for a week and then came
down to Berchtesgaden, where I intended to try to arrange an interview with Mr. Hitler the next time he came
to his mountain hideaway. We stopped at the inn, in the
bridal suite.

It rained for three days and three nights. We stayed
indoors all the time, read over and over the two maga-

zines the clerk had, and looked out of the windows at the water that fell everywhere. Drifting fogs obscured the mountains and the roofs of the houses. Raindrops danced in the puddles, small rivers ran down the streets, and Mr. Hitler stayed in Berlin.

The fourth day, we watched the proprietor of the inn play cards for an hour with the teacher, the local pharmacist, and the stationmaster. Then we looked out of every door and window at the rain, and then we began to drink beer. We had some in the dining-room and some in the lobby, where the card game was going on, and some in our room. We had a good deal before it was anywhere near time for lunch. In our room, Bride ransacked all the drawers in the bureaus, looking for anything, and found an almost empty bottle of American nail polish. He asked me its use. I explained it and then took off my shoes and fell asleep on the couch. When I woke up, Bride had just finished painting my toenails and was sitting on the floor in a corner, humming and accompanying himself on his guitar. I turned over and slept until two o'clock.

It was gray and cold, and we went down to the dining-room again. That room was an immense, vaulted hall on the side facing the street. Raised a few feet from the floor was a balcony. On a nice day, we could have sat there and looked out of the wide windows, over the valley and toward the high mountains. Now we turned the other way and looked at all the empty chairs and tables. Zenzi, the

waitress, brought us *Glühwein,* a good drink for such a
day. It is red wine served heated in a big goblet, with
some herbs in it. We drank slowly, dipping pieces of
bread into it. Later we just drank it and smoked cigars.
We did this for hours. Bride's two wet dogs slept under
the table all the while, and stank.

Toward nightfall a porter came in and dusted and

straightened a picture of Hitler which hung at the far
end of the hall, and then went out and came back with
two large Nazi flags. He draped these around the picture.
Another porter came in and together they carried out
most of the tables and arranged all the chairs facing the
picture, as if for a lecture or an entertainment of some
kind. Then two young men came in pushing a wheel-
barrow stacked with wreaths and garlands made of pine
branches, and with these they decorated the room. It began to smell like Christmas. Finally a radio and a loudspeaker were brought in and connected up. The loudspeaker was placed under the picture of Mr. Hitler.

The proprietor of the inn came to look things over and
we called him to our table on the balcony. He told us that
all this was in celebration of a National Socialist holiday,
that Herr Hitler was arriving in Berchtesgaden that
afternoon, and would make an address from his mountain
villa at eight o'clock. "Tomorrow will be a beautiful day,"
he said. *"Der Führer* always brings good weather with
him when he comes to Berchtesgaden."

Around seven-thirty the hall began to fill with men. We
had each had our seventh *Glühwein,* and I could not see
them very clearly, but I heard the sound of their heels
coming together in sharp greetings, the scraping of chair
legs on the wooden floor as they sat down, and a sound of
conversation—a deep murmur that came to my ears like
the word "Rhubarb, rhubarb," repeated over and over.

Bride seemed to be asleep. A song started the festivities
and I asked some men sitting a few yards from us if we
should leave, but they said no, very cordially, and invited
us to stay.

The Führer's address came over the loudspeaker and
lasted for an hour and a half. Then the *Horst Wessel*

Lied was sung, and when the men sat down again the local head of the Nazi Party stood before Hitler's picture and addressed the assembly.

His address was shorter than Hitler's. Toward the end of it he told how proud all of them were to be privileged to breathe the same clean German mountain air as the Führer himself, how honored they felt at being here in beautiful Berchtesgaden, so close to their Adolf Hitler, "who is right up there behind us." At these words, the speaker pointed in the general direction of Hitler's mountain villa. It seemed to me at the time that he was pointing directly at Bride and myself. As he did so, the members of the assembly turned around in their chairs, looked at us, and applauded.

In an ashtray on our table was a cold cigar butt about the size and shape of a small mustache. I stuck it under my nose, rose to my feet with great effort, and gave the Nazi salute. I also made a short speech. I can't remember what I said, but I screamed some words of encouragement in that hysterical tone, that falsetto pitch familiar to radio listeners all over the world.

There was a moment of silence when I sat down again; then the leader shouted, "*Schmeissen Sie das Schwein 'raus!*" and a beer glass sailed past my right ear. The next one must have hit me, for the rafters in the ceiling, the table, the uniforms, and Zenzi's big white apron all

became an uncertain black-and-brown picture. I remember that both of Bride's dogs barked and that Bride was carrying me somewhere, like a baby. I woke up the next morning in the bridal suite. Bride and his dogs and his guitar were gone.

It was, as the proprietor had promised, a lovely, sunny mountain morning. I put a cold towel on my head and walked out on the balcony. Down the street, behind an immense flag, came little girls marching in military formation and singing. At the far end of the street a rheumatic old prelate hobbled in haste to reach a side street to avoid having to salute the flag. I felt a hand on my shoulder, and when I turned around I saw two young men in civilian clothes. One of them identified himself as a member of the Gestapo and said, "Herr Bemelmans, come with us—very quietly and without attracting any attention whatever."

We walked through the town as friends would, without attracting any attention. We went straight to the rail-

road station, where one of the young men bought two
tickets, second class, to Munich; the other stayed behind,
I learned later, to call up Munich and tell somebody we
were on our way. After the train was rolling, the young
man with me pulled a small notebook from his pocket and
asked me to help him with his English. He was studying
English, he said, to help advance himself in the service of
the Gestapo. I helped him with it.

In Munich we went to the headquarters of the Gestapo,
which is in what used to be the Wittelsbach Palace. Here
I had to surrender my American passport. I was asked
some questions, and after an hour's wait, was taken to a
prison in the center of the city by another young man in
civilian clothes. Again we walked like friends and attracted
no attention. He carried in his hand a large envelope on
which was written in red ink, "Foreigner—Urgent." He
seemed to know about my case. "I am ashamed on your
behalf, Herr Bemelmans," he said to me on the way. "Why
don't you like Germany? Don't you see how fine everything is? Have you seen one single beggar? Have you seen
anyone badly dressed or in want? Have you seen anyone
hungry or idle? Has a train been late for you? Other
foreigners who come here and look around are full of
praises for the Third Reich, and for its Leader. You should
be ashamed, Herr Bemelmans!"

At the prison I was handed over to an official in uniform, who took me to a cell in which sat a small, pale

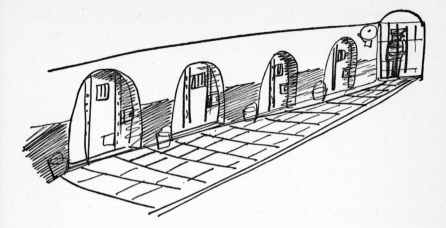

fellow who introduced himself to me as the former editor of a Catholic publication. He told me he had been in solitary confinement for six months. He was very eager and jumpy and talked fast. "You are, dear sir," he said, sitting close to me and taking hold of my hand, "the first person I have spoken to in all this time. I have been in this nice, bright cell only since yesterday—I think my case has come up for trial. Up to now I have not been informed of the charges against me. I have no lawyer; I don't even know what has become of my wife and my three children, but I am thankful to have someone to talk to."

He asked me why I was there. I told him my story and he said, "You won't be here long. An American citizen— how enviable, how fortunate for you! They will not dare to lock you up for long. You will walk on the streets this evening, or tomorrow evening, and hear the bells of the tramways and see people and eat in a restaurant and listen to the music playing. Of course you will get out— by seven o'clock tonight, I should think.

"But if anything should go wrong," he went on, gripping my shoulder with his hand, "and they lock you up alone as they did with me, then make yourself sit still, for heaven's sake. Don't start walking up and down, for you will walk around the earth in your cell; you will never be able to rest again. Another thing I will tell you that will help you: somewhere in your cell, on a wall, on the ceiling, perhaps on the floor, in some corner, at some time of the day or night when the light casts just the right shadows, you will find a place where an irregularity in the cement or the paint, a patch on the repair work, will outline for you the face of someone you love—your wife, your child, someone. It will take some imagination in the beginning, but after a while it will be there for you, strong and clear whenever you want it, to help you when the trembling starts, when the terror comes."

He seemed embarrassed by his own vehemence and stopped talking suddenly. I wanted to walk up and down but sat still out of deference to his advice. After a while a key turned in the lock and he whispered, "You see? I told you—they have come for you."

The keeper had my envelope under his arm. He took me to a waiting car and we drove to another prison of the

Gestapo in a suburb of Munich—a dirty old building with sweaty walls. I was handed over to the warden and he ordered a keeper to examine me.

An examination in a German prison is most thorough. The room in which it took place was as bright as a photographer's studio, with floodlights around the ceiling. There was a glass-covered table in the room, with a powerful light under the glass, and as I took off coat, vest, and trousers the keeper stretched them out on the table and examined the cloth, the lapels, every seam and pocket with the light shining through them. He asked for my shoes and almost took them apart. With a flashlight, next, he looked into my mouth, at the roof, then under the tongue, and into the spaces between the cheeks and the teeth. Then he asked for my underclothes. Finally he asked for my socks; I took them off and stood in front of him and the warden with my painted toenails.

The warden looked at me intently and then laughed. He pinched my cheek, called me "darling," and ordered that for the other prisoners' protection I be locked in a solitary cell. Doing a lopsided fandango, with one hand on his hip, the fingers spread fanwise, the warden danced out, shouting "Yoo-hoo!"

I was locked in a solitary cell.

In an hour I got something to eat. Through a small opening in the iron door came a ladle; I turned, and from it a heavy lentil soup, with small disks of sausage in it, poured into a battered tin bowl which I held under it. A hand reached in and gave me a large slice of black bread. Both the soup and the bread were good.

The light began to change after an hour or two more and I began to look for a patch on the wall, an irregularity in the floor or ceiling. Against the Catholic editor's advice, I had walked up and down several miles. Then the door opened and the warden told me, that he would have to release me, that the American consul was downstairs in his quarters with an official from the Gestapo.

I was released, and the consul advised me that I was to report to the State's Attorney the next morning. I got there promptly at nine. The State's Attorney was an affable, academic young man with a left cheek divided into six irregular fields by saber cuts. He received me in the outer room of a suite of offices under the inevitable picture of the Führer, but instead of the obligatory *"Heil Hitler!"* he said comfortably *"Grüss Gott!"* and offered me his hand in greeting. A one-armed secretary, a veteran with many decorations, brought my envelope and laid it on a desk. The State's Attorney pulled two chairs up to the desk, gave me a cigarette and lighted it for me, and waved the secretary out of the room. He began to speak, punctuating his sentences with a short, explosive, nasal "Ah-eh!"

"Ah-eh!" he said. "Disagreeable business, regrettable incident, Herr Bemelmans. Understandable, of course.

A glass too many. Can happen to any of us. Ah-eh! Your
—shall we call it pantomime?—should have been ignored,
of course. Some of our people, Herr Bemelmans, in a
sincere effort to—ah-eh!—serve the Party, are sometimes
overzealous. You chose, however, a particularly awkward
spot, Herr Bemelmans. Berchtesgaden is—ah-eh!—is the
last place for such a—but let that pass.

"This affair has, however, gone too far simply to dis-
miss it. The Party—that is, the State—cannot let you go
—ah-eh!—unpunished. The police cannot admit having
made—ah-eh!—a mistake. In order to put this matter out
of the way, I have permitted myself to make some calcu-
lations with which I hope you will find yourself in—ah-
eh!—agreement. There is a very good train for Berchtesgaden, leaving Munich Hauptbahnhof at seven-forty
tomorrow morning. They've reported the first snowfall in
Berchtesgaden; there's some excellent skiing around there;
Berchtesgaden is enchanting in late September. Ah-eh!
While you are there, Herr Bemelmans, I suggest that you
go to the District Court—I have written the address on
this slip of paper for you. It is only a few steps from the
station. In return for a small fee you will receive your
passport there.

"Ah-eh! As for the amount of the fine, what do you
think of, say, a hundred marks, Herr Bemelmans? Not
too much—very little. Ah-eh! A bagatelle for an American, what?"

I went back to Berchtesgaden, paid my fine at the District Court, and got back my passport. Coming out of the building, I saw Bride and his two dogs walking up the street. They were a block or so away and I stuck my fingers in my mouth and whistled. Bride turned and the dogs stopped in their tracks. He had his guitar under his arm and, standing against the background of snow, he looked, as always, like a souvenir-postcard picture of a Tirolian. It was my last glimpse of him. Bride's arm began to rise involuntarily as if in greeting, and then all at once he had turned and was running up into his mountains, his dogs after him, as if they had seen the devil.

CHAGRIN D'AMOUR

CHAGRIN D'AMOUR

Elegant, small, and endowed with all modern comforts, the Hotel Frankel in Port-au-Prince stands on the slope of a hill. The building has the appearance of a provincial baroque theater turned inside out. Its façade is an arrangement of foyers, balconies, boxes and loggias which are decorated with flowers and palms; all over it hangs a drapery of bougainvillea whose blood-colored blossoms seem to be made of tissue paper. The beds are neat and comfortable, the food and the service are excellent.

Two Frenchmen who lived in the room next to mine, and wore unpressed linen suits, were leaning over the balcony which we shared and looking at something below. When I walked out of my room, they straightened up for a moment and said good morning to me and as I joined them, they bent forward again.

The one close to me said in a hoarse whisper, pointing below with his chin, "What a magnificent woman!— Look at her—she isn't at her best in street clothes. In that sort of nurse's uniform she's wearing now she's extremely handsome, but you should see her in the water. I was bathing with her yesterday . . . She had on an old-fashioned suit, but she's all there; and when she comes out of the water, and the bathing suit clings to her . . ." He put the tips of the fingers of his right hand together and kissed them, closed his eyes for an instant and then looked up into the sky.

"I'd give anything . . ." he said, "it's all firm and white —white shoulders, white arms and soft snow-white knees —and where the bathing suit ends, over the knees, there was a faint pink ring . . ."

"Where the garter was," explained the other Frenchman.

They almost fell down to the floor below as they leaned out over the balcony rail again, and one of them plucked and dropped a bougainvillea blossom. It spiraled down slowly, floating past the beautiful nurse, companion or maid—whatever she was—who was playing chinka cheeks with a stout elderly lady. Mostly in white, with a very pink face; white hair, white lace, white shoes, white shawl —she was like the icing on a cake or the whitewashed front of the hotel.

By the time dinner was served, I had been introduced. The white lady was Mrs. Hamilton B. Hartford, American, from Rhode Island; the maid's name was Marie.

The tables at the Frankel stand out on the terrace in one straight line, and at dinner I sat at the one to the right of Mrs. Hartford. Mrs. Hartford ate alone.

Shortly after the soup was on the table a man in uniform appeared. He clicked his heels, bent over Madame Hartford's hand and said a well-spoken French good evening.

"Camille Blanchetaille," said Mrs. Hartford, by way of introduction; "Lieutenant Camille Blanchetaille."

Lieutenant Blanchetaille was dark and tall and smiled with a row of teeth so good that they looked unreal.

"Madame," he said, sitting down, "verily loves my country."

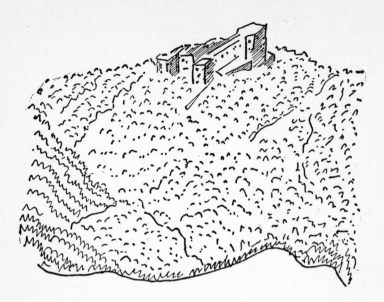

"*Ah, oui,*" said Mrs. Hartford, "yes, indeed I do—
c'est for-mi-dable, cette île."

"It's very lovely of you to say that, Madame Hartford," said the officer.

The waiter brought a dish and lifted a large cloche
from it. Manipulating a spoon and fork in his right
hand like a pair of pliers, he took a shell and placed it on
the plate in front of Madame.

"Ah, *les coquilles Saint-Jacques,*" said Madame Hartford. "*J'adore les coquilles Saint-Jacques. C'est formidable.*"

The lieutenant observed, "One eats very well here . . ."

and after a pause he added: "Are you going to visit the *Citadelle* this time, Madame?"

"*Ah, oui, toujours je visite la Citadelle, chaque fois que je viens ici je la visite. C'est for-mi-dable—la Citadelle.*"

"*Ah, oui, Madame, pour ça, vous avez raison, la Citadelle c'est vraiment formidable.*"

Madame turned to me and said: "I love Haiti. You know this is my fifth winter here."

And the lieutenant said in very broken English that he had the pleasure and honor to testify to that.

After the *coquille Saint-Jacques* was removed, the lieutenant asked Madame whether as a tourist and faithful visitor to Haiti, she found it completely satisfying. "I mean," he said, "as far as our poor efforts at making people happy here can go."

"*Ah, oui,*" said Madame. She was completely happy. After a while of musing, arranging her hair, and fanning herself, Madame Hartford said that there was only one thing that might be improved. "Just one thing . . ."

"And that is?" said the lieutenant, sliding forward in his chair and waiting politely.

"The donkeys," said Madame, "the treatment of animals in general—and of donkeys in particular. The peasants sometimes hit the donkeys savagely with their sticks. I do not like that at all. We visitors do not like that; we do not enjoy seeing that at all; we don't approve of cruelty to animals."

The lieutenant looked sympathetic, wrinkled his fore-head and said, "Madame, I am distressed to hear that, and we can do something about it; no doubt a way can be found, a plan, something must be devised. We cannot have that go on, certainly not."

"I have thought about it," said Madame Hartford.

"I have thought about it a good deal. First of all, the police should take away from the people any donkey that has been maltreated, and these poor, pitiful beasts could then be taken to a secluded spot, put into a sort of sanitarium for donkeys, on a small island perhaps, where they can rest and graze, where they can be properly fed, their wounds taken care of. The donkeys could stay there for a length of time that is commensurate with their condition."

"Ah, yes, certainly," said the lieutenant.

"If the animal is very thin and has been abused he will stay for a few months. If he has just been struck a few blows and is only a little tired and overworked—well, then he will stay for about a week. The proprietor of the donkey, in the meantime, will be put in jail for the same length of time, and will also pay a fine. These fines will be used to support the donkeys."

"Ah, Madame Hartford," said the official, "this is a most excellent and sensible idea. But we are very poor here, we have not the money to build this sanitarium for the poor animals."

"Oh—that part," Madame Hartford said, looking down at her hands. "I think we might perhaps arrange— I'm so fond of those little gray beasts that I might persuade myself to do something about it."

The lieutenant asked on what day Madame would visit the *Citadelle*, and suggested that the next week-end would be ideal because he was free then and would be glad to accompany her . . .

Madame Hartford was delighted to have him come and she hoped they would get well-fed and strong donkeys to ride upon.

Lieutenant Blanchetaille got up, bowed and walked to the back of the hotel.

After he was out of sight and hearing Madame Hartford leaned over toward the next table and said to its occupant: "He doesn't come here to see me at all, he comes on account of my Irish maid. Marie is a lovely girl, she is very beautiful, as perhaps you have seen—and she is a very fine type of girl—deeply religious, a Catholic of course."

At that moment one of the Frenchmen came down the stairs with a camera in his hand.

She's out in the garden somewhere," Madame Hartford said to the Frenchman and waved toward the back of the hotel where the lieutenant had disappeared. "Frenchmen," she said to her neighbor, "have a horrible time these days, and this one is the very finest type.

"But to get back to Marie . . . She has established an *entente cordiale* with Lieutenant Blanchetaille. I don't know what to do about it. You see them talking together; she's gone completely overboard for him. Last winter he came to New York to visit her. It was very difficult for the poor lad. They had to go and sit in the balcony of

the opera together, and I lost a good cook on account of
it. She wouldn't eat at the same table with them in the
servants' dining-room. The lieutenant is Catholic too.
I've tried to reason with them but you know what love is,
and it's true love in this case, on both sides. I hate to lose
her, but I will lose her, like cook. Marie wants to live here,
and she's studying French—there's her dictionary. She
carries it everywhere, and the trip up to the *Citadelle* is
just going to be a French lesson.

"These poor gray donkeys—or the *Citadelle*—or Chris-
tophe . . . do you think that young man cares anything
about all that? It's only so he can come to see Marie. He's
not interested in talking to an old woman. Here they
come!"

Marie asked for permission to go for a walk with him. They would be back before dark, she said. Together, they made a handsome picture, completely in order on this tropic isle.

"They are certainly proper," said Madame Hartford. "They will be back at nine, precisely. It's all very decent. They observe all the niceties. In fact if the lieutenant were white, or Marie were black, everything would be perfect and no one would be happier than myself.

"Ah!" said Madame Hartford touching up her coiffure and fanning herself, "*Le chagrin d'amour c'est for-mi dable.*"

HEAD-HUNTERS
OF THE QUITO HILLS

« 8 »

HEAD-HUNTERS OF THE
QUITO HILLS

THE day before we landed, the purser of the *Santa Lucia* gave all the passengers who were getting off at Guayaquil, a manifesto, prepared and issued by the Department of Immigration of Ecuador. Printed on good paper, decorated with a crest and written in four languages, it was a most polite invitation to visit upon arrival, or within the first twenty-four hours, the Chief of Immigration. His office, it said, was a few feet from the pier where we landed, right across the street from the Customs House. The purpose of the visit, the paper explained, was to allow the traveler to present his passport to the Chief and obtain from him advice and suggestions as to how to make his stay agreeable. The letter bore a magnificent signature under the words *"Honor y Patria."*

The next day, when we were to land, the doctor, a maroon-colored man with very small feet, came on board. The steward asked all passengers getting off at Guayaquil to assemble in the saloon. There were about forty of them and among those, I was the only non-Ecuadorian.

The doctor lifted his chin and his hands in a plea for silence, then in purest Castilian, his words arranged as carefully as his delicate hands, he informed the group that they all looked so well that he saw no need to examine anyone. He signed the ship's papers, closed his bag with a snap and accepted half a Hershey bar from a small boy. Holding it in one hand and putting his horn-rimmed glasses into the pocket of his coat with the other, he bowed and made his exit, backing out of the room. This was the first instance in which I experienced the great leniency of this wonderful land.

It was very early. Some of the passengers went back to bed, and others waited for breakfast in the foyer of the dining room. I was sitting alone in the lounge when a native appeared, one of the first to come on board to sell Panama hats and other souvenirs. He floated suddenly, soundlessly, and barefoot into the room. He looked around, and then from a woven basket produced a smaller woven basket and out of an inner nest of sacking took out a dark round object. He stroked a mane of blue-black, oily hair to one side, and there was a face. The native offered the shrunken head to me for three hundred and fifty *sucres*. I thanked him, but said I did not want it and he wrapped it up again. A Panama hat I did not want either. Panama hats are not made in Panama but in Ecuador. I had bought three of them because they are so

cheap. None of them fits; two are too small and one is too
big. I told him I had a Panama hat and he disappeared.

At about nine I went down the steep stairs that hung
on the side of the boat to go ashore. I took a launch
named *Gloria*. It was painted blue. We soon passed a
battleship which was moored in the Guayas River. While
we were in the shadow of this vessel, the man who was
steering the launch took hold of the wheel with his bare,
right foot, leaned forward and removed a pillow from
the seat. He opened a small locker and out of it he took
a box in which lay a shrunken head. He wanted two hundred *sucres*, then a hundred and eighty *sucres*, and finally
one hundred and fifty *sucres* for it. He brushed the black,
dry hair with his hand, wrapped it around the face again

and put the head back in the box with the pillow over it. He took the wheel in his hands and brought his launch up against the pier. I went to the Grand Hotel, left my bags there and then repaired to the office of the Chief of Immigration.

The building in which he officiates is the most ambitious in Guayaquil. It stands next to a statue of General Sucre, and the Department of Immigration is at the end of a long corridor paved with polished tiles. The visitor is reflected in them as he walks along and every step he makes echoes three times. As I approached a clerk rose from his desk at the end of the passage. I carried the manifesto in my hand. He ran into a room and came back with another man; both of them smiled, and the better dressed of the two advanced toward me and opened his arms wide. "I am happy to see you. You have come to see me, no? You know I send out these papers to everybody, but no one, nobody pays any attention to them, you are the first one," he held up a finger, "in one month to come here. Take a seat." He spoke then of the beauty of Ecuador, recommended various trains and hotels, suggested excursions, alligator hunts, mineral baths, safaris into the jungle, and finally asked me to go along with him to a luncheon for a newly arrived diplomat, a man from another South American country.

He excused himself for a moment and went to get his hat. As soon as the Chief was out of the room, his assist-

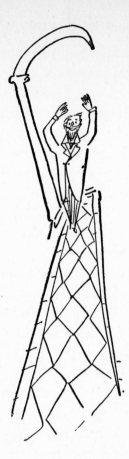

ant opened a drawer in his desk, that drawer in which
people in American offices usually keep a cake of soap and
a towel, and I thought he would bring out a shrunken
head, but he only gave me a card on which was the address
of a store where shrunken heads, Panama hats, and rings
carved out of ivory were for sale. "Go there with confi-

129

dence," he said, "you will get a very fine one, reasonably. Tell them I sent you, here, I will put my name down."

We arrived at the hotel where a flower-laden table awaited us. I lifted my Panama hat, and the Chief, in Spanish, offered a greeting difficult to match. He and the diplomat embraced each other as two people starting to dance—first to the right side, then to the left, and finally as if bumping into each other face on, while they continually patted each other's shoulders. The official then stood away a foot and a half and sang, "Most distinguished and estimated, cultured and noble and not-sufficiently-celebrated sir and friend, welcome to Ecuador." We sat down.

The menu was written in Spanish and in violet ink. It said:

MENU

CREMA SAN GERMAN

CALDO AL NATURAL

CORVINA COCIDO CON SALSA DE ALCAPARRAS

PAPAS FRITAS

PASTELITOS DE YUCA

SALÓN EN SALSA DE TOMATE

ENSALADA MIXTA DE LEGUMBRES

ARROZ   MENESTRA

PASTEL DE COCO

CAFE

Julio 1/1940

I understand Spanish well enough but speak it badly. The food was indifferent and the wine bad; the headwaiter, a halfbreed, had hands like a baker and a shirtfront with tomato spots on it. His hair hung over his collar and into his face; he looked out of the window most of the time.

I called him for a match; I had no match or lighter. Ecuador has a match law; one cannot bring any matches or lighters into the country without special permission. The diplomat had a lighter but there was no alcohol in it. After a while the headwaiter called a waiter who brought some Ecuadorian matches, manufactured by the government plant, the *Estanco de Fosforos*. The waiter opened the box. The matches were of a dark wood, some of them split and others bent. The first one he tried to light broke in his fingers; the second he threw away; the third lit up with a sudden explosion—a small torch-like flame appeared, made a "Ffffhhhssss," and then, leaving a ribbon of thick, milky smoke, went out. Out of six more matches, two gave light. In the explosion of one of them, small fragments from the head of the match shot away, one on my cheek and another on my hand where they burned with brief intensity, like the sting of a wasp. Finally my cigarette, labeled *Welcome* and made of dark, sweet tobacco, was lit. The waiter bowed down once more, waving the dead match, and muttered something. "No," I said, "Thank you very much. I have a Panama hat and I don't want a shrunken head either." He reached for the

131

mineral water, which comes here in Perrier-shaped bottles and costs five cents a quart, and said that he had a
very curious shrunken head, one with white hair and white
eyebrows, very rare. I brushed the breadcrumbs from my
trousers and got up and thanked him again. I said I had
to go to the barber.

The Chief of Immigration had recommended a very
good one. This barber, in a very aseptic shop on one of
the main streets of Guayaquil, was fortunate in having a
most beautiful manicurist, a young tropical woman with
fatal allure. The barber stuck a finger in my month to be
able to scrape better over my cheeks. He pushed my nose
up, and made agonized faces while he shaved me. After
stropping his razor for a second attack, he suddenly left
me soaped in and under the sheet. In a few moments he
came back with a shrunken head. He held it so that I could
see it in the mirror which was suspended diagonally over
my chair. I shook my head. He raised his eyebrows first,
then one shoulder and put the head away. All this time, a
dark brown boy, not more than six years old, had been
shining my shoes.

I left the barbershop and walked back to the hotel.
The boy who had shined my shoes ran after me, shouting,
"*Patron, Patron.*" When he caught up with me, he pulled
my sleeve. I told him that I did not want to buy a
shrunken head. "No, *patron*, no shrunken head," he said,
"the girl, the manicurist, she loves you. You want to buy

the key? Is only twenty *sucres*." Half a dozen children stood around now, some selling lottery tickets, others wanting to shine my shoes once more, and I said, "No, thank you." They all followed me to the hotel.

"Is only ten *sucres* now, the key," whined the little boy. "She love you very much."

The diplomat and I left on the train for Quito, the capital, the next morning. Our seats were reserved in the observation car. The diplomat said that his reception at Guayaquil had been very nice but he had had a much more elaborate and festive one in the last South American republic he had served. There, he said, they had sent the president's personal railroad car for him. He described this as an eighteenth-century drawing room on wheels, with carmine upholstery, brass beds, and large brass spittoons. It was supplemented with every modern comfort; it had not only a bathtub, but also a *bidet* and a shaving mirror on a movable arm. He had sat in it, among the bouquets and telegrams which had been sent to greet him, for about two hours. Then he grew restive, looked out of the window and asked the Chief of Protocol, who had been sent to travel with him, when the train would leave. The Chief of Protocol was embarrassed. He said he should have explained it all long ago and he regretted very much that it was such a stupid arrangement, but, although they had a presidential car, they did not have a presidential locomotive. The car would not move till it could be attached to the regular train which left the next morning.

Outside of the conductor, no one tried to sell us a shrunken head until the train stopped at Alausi. A railroad employee came into the car and offered a *Zanza* head again. The diplomat took it, turned it around, brushed the hair apart at the back of the head, and explained to me that it was a fake. One can always tell that they are fakes when they are sewn up in back of the skull. Furthermore, he told me that having been stationed both in Colombia and Peru, he knew about shrunken heads and had a fine collection of them which he would show me in Quito. "Don't buy one until you can recognize the real ones," he said. "Be very careful when buying shrunken heads, there are some good imitations made." For the rest of the trip he told me about head shrinking. He had made frequent trips into the jungles of the Oriente, been among the Jivaro Indians and, while he himself had never been fortunate enough to witness the ceremony by which these heads were obtained, scientists who had studied the Indians and their customs agreed that the procedure was something like the following:

If a warrior wants a shrunken head, he must bring home the body of an enemy whom he has killed in battle. The chief of the tribe and everyone in the camp gather around. After long and elaborate rites, the warrior cuts the head off the body with two sharp incisions below the jaws, leaving the neck on the body. The head is then placed on a *pingi nuka* leaf, a second *pingi nuka* leaf is placed on top, and the warrior sits down on the head, while the chief of the tribe blows tobacco juice up his nostrils to make him immune from any evil that the spirit of the dead man may be planning. After this, the skin is carefully peeled from the skull and parboiled in a tea brewed from various herbs. The face, at this stage, looks like a dirty washrag with ears, two slits where the eyes were, a mouth and a wrinkled part that was the nose. The hair is still left on the scalp. The inside of the face is then carefully scraped, and the head filled with hot pebbles which are allowed to cool. This operation is repeated several times until the head gradually shrinks to about the size of an orange. When it is small enough it is parboiled again and once more filled with hot pebbles. While it is drying the warrior models the face, like a sculptor, and sets the features right. When it is quite dry and hard, the pebbles are shaken out of it and it is dyed black with charcoal. The eyes and lips are sewn up with the fiber of the *chonta* palm. It is then stuck on a lance and the Indians dance around it, shout at it, and strike it, while the warrior tells the story of the battle in which he killed the owner of the head. If the warrior has been lucky enough to capture the wives of his enemy as well, he takes them to himself, and they now sit through all the ceremony, wailing in chorus. If he has not captured any widows, he appoints his own wives to wail as proxies. The head itself is eventually forgotten, or sold to traders.

When we arrived in Quito, I found that the best hotel in that city, the Metropolitano, was filled, so I went to the other, the Savoy. The light switches in this hotel are outside of the guests' rooms in the corridor, a neat and clever invention, I thought; the guest turns the light on inside his room while he is still outside, and walks into a bright apartment. The invention has one drawback, however. When the guest is in bed, he finds he must get up and walk outside to turn the switch off again and then light a match to find his way back to bed. I had just got back to my bed the first night when the light was turned on again from outside. The door opened slightly and a bell-boy crept in. He brought some towels and clean water and then came close to my bed. He pulled out a package from under his white jacket, undid a lot of white paper, and out of it brought a Panama hat. As he unfolded it, he almost dropped the inevitable shrunken head. He wanted a hundred *sucres* for it. I looked at it, and it was sewn up the back. He left and came back with a real one. For that he wanted three hundred *sucres;* it was yellowish, with an agonized expression, and short hair. I did not buy that one either.

In the rear of the Hotel Metropolitano is a small kiosk dedicated to the sale of souvenirs. The next shrunken heads I saw were there on a string, a dozen of them hang-

ing in a row behind the window. They seemed related to
each other, and happy, almost laughing. They hung over
some gourds decorated with landscapes, pictures of Indians, several plaques with the profile of an Indian chief,
and paintings of volcanoes, stuffed toucans, and souvenir
postcards. Some of the heads were gray-haired, and two

of them were women. The price was one hundred *sucres*, and upon examination I found that they all were sewn up in back of the skull. When the owner of this shop saw me turn from them, he confided that he had real ones too. In back of his establishment, out of the drawer of a desk, he took two real heads, both of them pale and with the same miserable mien as that of the one the bell-boy had shown me the night before. When I declined these, he said that he had a very real one, and after more hide and seek among his wares and souvenirs, he brought out an excellent specimen, truly beautiful, wild and authentic, with thick hair, the Indian face in perfect miniature. He asked five hundred *sucres* for it.

I met the diplomat a while after and he showed me his collection of genuine heads and he told me that he would take me to see a place where the fakes came from. We drove to the outskirts of Quito and then left the car in an impassable alley halfway up the mountain, Pichincha. There we found a little earthen house. It was surrounded by a wall on which plants and flowers and grasses grew in profusion.

In the courtyard stood a little man, half-Indian, half-white. He wore a blue smock and was surrounded by his works, his wife, and ten children. The whole family stopped working to greet us. They had been busy on some of the plaques that were for sale below. The manufacture of these was geared to an almost North American tempo; on two long shelves that reached from one end of the garden to the other, disks, pressed out of plaster, lay in rows. On every disk was the profile of an Otavalo Indian playing the pipes of Pan. The father had a brush in his hand. He sharpened the end of the brush, twisting it between his lips, and then started down the line. In one passage he put eyebrows on all the Indian profiles. He came back, hopping from plaque to plaque and stopping a second in front of each, and when he was done all the chiefs had an eye. His wife, more phlegmatic, wandered along the line putting carmine on the cheeks. The children were busy with other things; one mixed paints, another sawed coconuts carefully into slices, a third removed the white meat from the rings thus obtained, and a fourth fitted the coconut ring as a frame around the already finished plaques. Last, a little girl tied on ribbons to hang them up by.

"I am sorry my eldest are not here; my sons, Alfonso and Arquimedes, are out hunting," said the father. He offered us some *pisco,* and the diplomat said nice things to the baby. It was tied to the back of a girl of about five who was stacking up coconuts. Then he asked the busy man to show us how he made shrunken heads. He was reluctant for a while but, on taking another drink, eventually agreed to take us to his inner sanctum. This was another workshop which gave proof to the order and efficiency of this enterprising artisan. Here were rows of shelves again, and on them shrunken heads. He showed us three clay faces that wore the contented and smiling expressions of the Indians that hung in the window of the kiosk. He explained how he modeled pieces of goatskin over these. He left the hair of the goatskin on the part which was to cover the heads and shaved the parts that were to be faces; two little bars of hair were also left over the eyes. These he trimmed with manicure scissors so that they formed eyebrows; one can detect fakes immediately by this, because the hair on both eyebrows grows in the same direction and not away from the nose as on real faces. He said that he made about ten heads out of one goat. He marked the skin off with chalk like a tailor divides cloth. The mouth and eyes he cut out with a razor blade. Madame or his oldest daughter, Carmen, then sewed them up with real *chonta* fiber; the whole thing is then dyed black, except for the ones he leaves white, a rarity of his own invention. He admitted that they went very well with tourists. The heads are sold in Quito and in other places for one hundred *sucres*, of which he gets fifty; the Indian profiles for twenty-five, landscapes of Quito, of Otavalo, of Pichincha, and Chimborasso anywhere from fifty to a hundred. We bought some landscapes. They were not without charm, flat primitives whose coloring with much blue and white in them is reminiscent of the murals in Italian restaurants.

He was proud of the sale and offered us more *pisco*, drinking out of the bottle himself because there was only one glass. Then he told us that he had been able to cut down the expense of making these heads somewhat by a surprising discovery, by using the pelt of an animal that was less expensive than a goat—a pelt out of which he also got ten heads, but with hair much softer than a goat's, almost human. He reached into a hammock and brought out a black fur. He said it was from a totally unknown animal and that he obtained the skin directly from the Indians of the upper Amazon. He let me feel it, and I spread the skin on the floor.

We said good-by. Night sets in quickly in Quito; it is almost dark at about seven p.m. the year round. As we left, two young men came up out of the city. They were panting from the steep climb and one had a sack slung over his shoulder. "Ah, my eldest are here," said the little man. "Come, Alfonso, and you Arquimedes." He introduced them and the younger one put down the sack. A dog fell out of it, one of those mongrels with long, soft hair that one sees running with the Indians through the streets of Quito.

We said good-by once more to Señor Pazmino. On the way down to Quito, the diplomat told me that the unhappy, yellowish heads one sees occasionally were heads obtained out of graves, with the aid of attendants in the morgues. Most of them were the heads of infants. This practice had ceased, he told me, partly because the shrinking is a good deal of trouble but chiefly because the tourists prefer the pretty ones.

VACATION

« 9 »

VACATION

In the fat, dead days of tires and gasoline I always tried to leave New York about four, in order to get out of the Holland Tunnel close to five. The ride over the Pulaski Skyway at that hour is one of the most exciting parts of a trip to the South. In the gaseous stretches of the Jersey landscape, half of it gone in shadows, stand drawbridges, factories, electric plants, and immense tanks. They have the beauty of the devil, with green and yellow flames leaping from chimneys, with trains smearing black smoke over a gray horizon. The landscape is framed in a loop of light, an endless gleaming necklace, rolling over the hills and bridges, that is made up of headlights of oncoming cars. In snow or rain it is doubly enchanting. It is not all gas and oil and stink. We even saw a rabbit.

Barbara, who sat beside me, had her nose flattened against the window and saw the rabbit first. He scampered across the highway in the direction of Newark.

"Pappy!"

"Yes, darling."

"Tell me a story about a rabbit. A story about a rabbit, a rabbit, a rabbit."

Once upon a time, a monkey and a rabbit met. The monkey said to the rabbit that it was a pity that he, the rabbit, could never sit still, but always had to look in back of him.

"Ha!" said the rabbit, "how about yourself? You can't sit still either, you always have to scratch yourself."

Both of them then agreed that for one whole day, from sunrise to sunset, they would sit side by side, and the rabbit would not look around, and the monkey would not scratch himself.

The day on which they were going to do this arrived,

and at the moment the sun rose the rabbit and the monkey met and sat down side by side.

Without batting a lid, the rabbit quietly looked down at the grass in front of him. The monkey sat still, his hands folded in his lap. They remained in this position for hours. The time passed very slowly, and it was midday when the monkey, who knew he could no longer sit still, said to the rabbit, "When I was a soldier, bullets hit me here, and here, and there, and there—" and wherever he pointed, at that spot on his body he quickly scratched himself.

The rabbit was no better off. He felt that he could not look another second at the grass in front of him, and he also began telling a story. "When I was a soldier," he said, "the enemy was hard after me. To escape him I had to jump like this, and like that, to the left and to the right." Like lightning, his eyes followed the motions of his limbs and every time he jumped he looked back.

Barbara, who was four years old, was asleep when I explained the moral of the story.

Before I fell asleep myself, we stopped at the Anglers' Rest in Seaford, Delaware. I tried to persuade the waitress who served us to bring Barbara some milk and vegetables, but Barbara didn't want any milk and vegetables.

"Well, honey, you can have spaghetti and meat balls," said the girl. "But why don't you order a submarine sandwich? My, that's good! Mmm."

"What is a submarine sandwich?"

"Well, a submarine sandwich comes two ways, the 15¢ one is seven inches long, and for a quarter you get one twelve inches long——"

"What's it made of?"

"It's made of Italian cheese, salami, Italian seasoning, hot peppers, lettuce, and spiced ham; the cheese is put down first and then olive oil is put over it—it comes in a specially baked loaf of Italian bread."

Barbara ordered it, and ate it, all of it, all of the 15¢ one, and drank some of my beer with it.

I wanted a cigar with my coffee. The girl brought me a cigar almost as long as the sandwich, mustard-colored, with large ribs running through the wrapper. It lit up like a torch, and when I asked her whether she had any other kind she said, "No, honey, just a 5¢ one."

I asked for the bill. She wrote it on a piece of paper called "Guest check." She stuck a pencil in her hair and turned a knob on the radio.

A voice wailed, "Like a fool I didn't believe him and all the time I had a couple of detectives follow him. Why do I always have to hurt the people I love and why, why do the worst things always happen to the swellest people?"

"Good night, honey," said the waitress, and we left and drove to the Norfolk ferry.

Someone told me that you could go aboard the ferry

boat at about eleven, get a room and bath, and cross during the night, arriving in Norfolk at 7 a.m. The cabin
looked like an illustration out of Dickens, the cast-iron
bathtub was just large enough for Barbara, and the beds
were two-story army bunks. However, the ferry saves
time.

The next day, I followed the Ocean Highway, and
turned inland as soon as it got warmer.

In New Orleans, Barbara was fascinated by another

sandwich. This one was called "Martin's poorboy sandwich." She saw it in a little shop—outside of which hangs a sign showing a small boy who eats a sandwich larger than himself. A twenty-eight-inch loaf of bread is cut in half, loaded with sliced roast beef, lettuce, and tomato, and the whole is soaked in gravy and costs 10¢. The sandwiches, which are sold in several establishments, were invented during the Depression, and have made their inventor, a legless man, so rich that a colored chauffeur carries him from one "poorboy" place to the other. I refused, however, to go in there and buy two "poorboys," and so we arrived in tears at Antoine's Restaurant.

This exquisite and sufficiently esteemed restaurant is all that one expects of it. It is blessed with a proprietor who honors his profession and worships his ancestors (I have counted 53 photographs of them on menus, on souvenirs, on postcards, and in frames). He has a maître d'hôtel who is one of the few in that difficult calling who is free of all pomp. We ate in the 1820 Room, a private apartment in which hangs a large oil painting of Madame Antoine, a kind of Frau Sacher. Barbara was particularly elated because in a glass case along the wall of the room, among various personal belongings of Antoine Alciatore, the founder (1840–1885), there a pair of baby shoes, the first pair he wore, kept right next to his shaving mug.

M. Isidor Cassou, the good headwaiter, an Adolphe
Menjou type, supervised the dinner, and I had a terrible
time because I had to eat the *spécialité de la Maison, les
huîtres Rockefeller.* I detest nothing so much as oysters
when they are cooked, and these were covered with a
green mud, and done *au gratin.* During the ordeal, M.
Roy L. Alciatore, the grandson of Antoine, showed me a
photograph in which he was shown eating the millionth
order of this dish. I ate them quickly, almost swallowing

the shell. M. Alciatore beamed and had a second order brought in.

The rest of the menu was superb cooking, particularly the pompano. It's an honest restaurant—the lights go out every time someone orders crêpes Suzette. The kitchen is badly lit; the chef stands in front of an old coal stove and cooks in heavy casseroles; everything is as it should be, and I hope it will forever stay that way, including the cedar sawdust that is sprinkled on the floor. It fills the rooms with an appetizing perfume. It smells like pencils being sharpened.

The road from New Orleans to Marco Island, where we went to go fishing, runs along the Gulf of Mexico and is in excellent condition. It will remain in Barbara's memory as a long line of dead black pigs. She counted fourteen of them. These pigs roam the country, half wild, and

then, crossing the road, they are run over by the fast-moving cars. I had to tell several pig stories.

The captain of the fishing boat on Marco Island was

very co-operative. He said, "I used to go barefoot, but now the place is getting fashionable, and out of consideration for the lady of the house, I wear shoes." We ran into a lot of fish, and I observed how much they resemble people.

Pulling them in became tiresome labor and at the end of it my arms hurt and the fishbox overflowed with them —all of them silently gulping. I wanted to let them go, but the captain said he could make something of them, fertilizer, I think.

Miami is Miami, and by no other name is there a city such as this. The hotel employees were as efficient and quick as dentists, and fingerprinted besides. Everything is to be had here from caviar to a Goodyear blimp. From a point of design and efficiency the new hotels in Miami Beach are models.

The main highway to Palm Beach was now an unending, open-all-night string of tourist cabins, orange and papaya juice pavilions, sea shells, carved coconuts, and cypress-knee souvenir stands. There is another, quiet road along the ocean, one of the finest drives in the world.

An unforgettable picture presented itself to me at a turn in that road. It was past the S curve that leads to the Hutton castle in Palm Beach. This edifice always reminds me of an advertisement for breakfast food. I am certain that at night gnomes work there under the stairs of the baronial halls and in the vaulted cellars

wrapping crunchy crackies, full of golden goodness, into bright packages and mailing them out in Josef Urban boxes.

The castle's garden faces the unceasing sound of the waves; the moon shone through the long, thin fins of palm leaves, and on a bulkhead near the sea sat a black gardener and a maid, engaged in ardent courtship. Beyond them, two tugs tried to get a steamer off a sandbank.

In Charleston, we stopped at a frequently and highly

recommended restaurant. It is down near the slave market, and called Henry's. It is a restaurant of indifferent décor, which is often the sign of a very good place. On the tiled floor stood old Viennese bentwood chairs. The lighting fixtures are like those used in barber shops, and in the right rear corner of the restaurant's main dining-room was a group of darkies—waiters arranged according to size, the small ones in front, the tallest in back leaning against the sideboard. I thought they were about to sing some spirituals, but they were asleep with eyes wide open.

One of them exiled himself from the group and slouched over to our table. "There is two kinds of chowder on the menu," he said, "a blackfish chowder and a special one, a Charleston chowder." We ordered one of each, and when they were served they looked and tasted exactly alike, a white, sloppy paste, flavorless and lukewarm.

The next thing, some seafood which was recommended as a native dish, and *spécialité de la Maison*, turned out to be another stew, a kind of *rijstafel* with small fish scales that got between your teeth, and other foreign substances thrown in.

On this trip we stayed at several hotels that belong to a chain which is owned by a man named Dinkler. They are a kind of traveling-salesman hotel, very clean and satisfactory. In each of them, in the center of immense lobbies, stands a statue of the founder—a grim-visaged executive. On everything is printed "this is a Dinkler Hotel," and the doorman sends you to the next Dinkler.

On the highway that leads to Newcastle and back to New York is a hill. When I was halfway down it a green traffic light shone ahead. A car approached from the left over a crossroad and got stuck in the snow. Under the light, the hill was solid ice and it was too late to do anything. I pushed Barbara, who sat next to me, down on the floor, and then the crash came. The driver of the truck and his helper, two natives of Dover, were shaken up. The driver had a cut over his left eye, and we all had to go to a magistrate.

The driver and his helper were greeted by the magistrate as John and Charlie, and everyone told the story of the accident. The magistrate listened carefully to all three versions and then he leaned back and asked a few questions. He seemed an honest man and he looked out of the window somewhat bewildered. It was a difficult case to decide. He asked a state trooper to drive him to the spot where the accident had taken place, and when he came back he lit a pipe and looked out of the window some more.

The driver sat on a bench in front of us, near an iron pot-belly stove. He adjusted a small bandage over his eye. A little blood ran down over his face, and he wiped it away. The room was silent.

Barbara watched the man wipe the blood away. Then she said, "Pappy, why did you try to kill that poor man?"

The magistrate smiled gratefully. Nodding to me, he knocked on the table and said,

"Guilty!"

CHER AMI

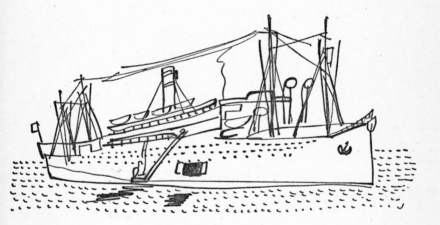

10

CHER AMI

To work for me, to live with me, is hard. I am composed of disorderly habits. I live the way William Saroyan thinks people live, and it's not so funny off the stage. Normally, I am filled with the greatest good-will toward my fellow men, and I manifest this with generous gestures in all directions. I stop and smile at children, and I spread breadcrumbs for the pigeons on the stairs of Saint Patrick's, but the next day I would like to kick them all in the shins.

My habitat is mostly bars and restaurants, hotels and depots, and the lobbies and entrances thereof. In normal times I am found on the decks of steamships, and on the shores of tropic isles. I arrive suddenly, somewhere far away, and once there I haunt the piers and terminals and curse if there isn't a boat or plane to take me back immediately. I get homesick as soon as I am away from where I've gone—going it's for New York, coming back it's for where I've left. To share such a life, one needs a mobile servant, adaptable as a chameleon, shock- and surprise-proof, a person who gazes into your face as into a crystal ball and then knows whether to come close or stay away from you the rest of the day. The coin is not too good, either.

The ideal servant for me is a kind of Sancho Panza, a companion and friend with the melancholy kinship of an Irish setter. The run-of-the-mill retainer won't do at all; no Treacher type, no Admirable Crichton for me. I'd rather have him inept as far as service goes, but let him make it up with perfection in all the other departments. Above all, let him be someone curious and different. My ideal would be an ex-sergeant of the Foreign Legion, or a bankrupt banker, a retired road-company leading man who could mug Hamlet and Shylock, or a third-rate Karloff. Give me a burglar, or even a dismissed G-man, anything, but not the meek soul to whose life a million polished teapots are a monument.

My wishes are usually fulfilled with miraculous promptness, sometimes with such dispatch that I get scared at the prompt benevolence that hovers over me.

For example, I wished for this fol-de-rol butler, and not very hard either. I did not go to any employment agency to look for him; I did not even put an ad in the paper, nor did I ask anyone if they knew of such a man. I just wished, and he came.

I met him in Haiti last winter. For a while I lived in the *dépendance* of a small hotel, the rooms of which were like the cells in an exquisitely run insane asylum. Every compartment had its own precise garden of tropical greenery. Planted in the exact center of each of these eight-by-twelve-foot gardens was a tree, not large enough for anyone to use it for climbing in or out of the garden, but with enough leaves to shade a rattan *chaise longue*, and with four branches for birds to sing on in the twilights of morning and evening. Each of the gardens was enclosed by a white high wall.

The floor of the bedroom was a mosaic of black and white tile, and in its center stood a bed with tortured cast-iron ornaments, small knobs, and buns, spirals and little brass blossoms stuck and twisted on its head- and foot-boards. During the day, the design of the bed was somewhat diffused under a tent made of mosquito netting, which was attached to the ceiling by a rope and pulley. At night, one was under the tent, and then the fancy ironwork was beautifully clear.

The morning after the night when I wished for the companion, I beheld on awakening the outline of a man outside the mosquito tent. It seemed that he had stood there for a long while. He was in a state of repose, leaning on the wall, and he threw the butt of a cigarette out into the garden when he saw me sit up. On his head was a Chevalier straw hat. I lifted the netting, and, leaning out of bed, I observed that my visitor was barefoot and sunburned, and that his hat was honored with the bright colors of a Racquet Club band. He had a lean, generous

face, and looked somewhat like a skiing teacher or a dere-
lict tennis pro. Over his lips lay a black mustache, and his
shirt was without buttons. The sleeves were torn off halfway between the elbow and the shoulders, offering ventila-
tion to his chest.

He sat down at the foot of the bed and told me that he was my friend. He told me his name and informed me that he was one of a group of escaped prisoners from Devil's Island, and that he was taken care of, with his companions, by the good *Sœurs de la Sagesse*. He and the boys lived at the convent . . .

He corrected himself and explained that he and the others were not escaped criminals in the strict sense of the word, but that since the Vichy Government was unable or unwilling to pay the upkeep of the prison or the salaries of the administrators and guards at Guiana, the prison doors had simply been left open, and whoever wanted to, left.

"I," he continued, "was a *doubleur;* that is, I had served my sentence, but had to stay on the Island. We left French Guiana, my friends and I, in a sixteen-foot *canot*. No one tried to stop us. We were twelve when we started. The hardest part was to get straight out to sea past the reef which is called the Frenchmen's Grave. To pass this, you have to go over sand-bars in a straight line for about thirty-five kilometers, and then you turn left.

"That takes courage. We did it all with the aid of a map, which we had copied, and with the aid of a Greek, a seaman who knew the stars. We also had a small compass with us, and we got as far as Trinidad. It was easy. A captain of a ship must find a port; we only tried to

165

find the land. The Governor of Trinidad gave us eighty
dollars to buy a bigger boat, and with that we got as far
as Jamaica. Now we are here and thinking of going on
to Cuba. We have a tolerably good life here. Twice a week
we watch the plane come in, that is where I saw you
arrive. We sit in the convent garden or along the water
most of the time, and the *bonnes sœurs de la Sagesse* take
care of us as if we were little birds, but it's not a life for
a man.

"*Cher ami*," he said, "do something for me. I am a
pastry cook, I have been a hotel director. I know how to
drive a car and how to fix it. I can write on the machine.
I can steer a boat. I am ready to go anywhere, and I am
afraid of nothing. Give me a little food and pocket money,
and I am your man, your servant, your friend for life."

He lounged back on the bed, lit a cigarette, spread his
toes fanwise, folded his hands in back of his head, and
looked up at the ceiling, waiting for my answer.

"I wanted to talk to you last night," he added after a
while. "I followed you from the cinema up to your hotel,
but I thought you might get scared or nervous, so I came
this morning."

He broke the few moments of silence, in which I thanked
that particular department of Providence that concerns
itself with me, by remarking that if I was worried about
his past he could put me completely at ease. He confessed
that when he was young, he had made a mistake—he had

disemboweled his mistress. Ah, Simone was a very beautiful girl, but she had been unfaithful, and he was not sorry.

I told him he could start in right away. He could pack my trunk and take it to the ship; and as soon as he got to New York, there were several people I would like to have disemboweled, but nicely, and I would give him a list every Monday. I gave him a small advance, and then I said that the only thing I was worried about was how he would get to New York, past the immigration authorities, the police, and J. Edgar Hoover's sharp-eyed and resourceful young men.

"Bah! Leave that to me," he said. "I shall be in New York—let me see—it's the middle of August now; give me until the end of September. It's child's play. About the twenty-fifth of September, I would say. Where do you live?" I gave him my address, and that afternoon he arrived with a boy to carry my trunk which he had neatly packed. On the way to the boat, he stopped the car at the *Magasin de Mille Cent Choses* and bought a pack of razor blades, which he said I needed; and then he said good-by and *au revoir*. He slowly shook my hand and lifted the Chevalier straw hat. He waved it so hard when the ship pulled out that the Racquet Club band came off and fell into the bay. A native boy dove after it, and he gave him a coin.

"Wonderful, wonderful," I said to myself and missed

him immediately. Stretched out in my deck-chair, I thought how very fortunate I was. When I got home, I was still gloating over the fact that I had found the perfect man.

One morning soon after my return, I found a letter.

It started: "La Havane, Cuba. *Cher ami,* I have the honor to address these few words to you, to inform you that, after a sudden departure from Haiti in a boat which I and a few of the others who shared my idea procured along the waterfront, we proceeded for Cuba. The beginning of the voyage was without incident. One night, however, we had some difficulty holding our direction, as a violent wind caused our leaking shell to dance an infernal sarabande on the waves.

"Without the sail and the mast, and also without the man who steered the boat at the outset, without a rudder even, the wind delivered us to the eastern shore of Cuba, and, to make our *misère* perfect, into a nest of waiting gendarmes from whom we were too wet and exhausted to flee. My companions and I find ourselves detained at the *Centre d'Émigration,* and I regret to inform you that my departure from here can only be effected by the immediately-sent sum of one hundred dollars. I will consider the hundred dollars in lieu of six months of service."

I sent him the money. I have faith in such characters, and they have never failed me. Neither did *Cher Ami.*

In the middle of one night when I lay awake, I had one of my rare moments of worry again. Suppose, when he turns up, I said to myself, he's the perfect servant, butler, and companion, and besides, a good pastry cook. Suppose he's out in the pantry one day squeezing many happy returns on my birthday cake when there is a knock at

the door, and it's the police. Then follows the story of the body of a young woman, partly decomposed, found crammed into the luggage compartment of my convertible coupé . . . O.K. take him away; but he won't come quietly . . . smack, smack, *klunk;* I hold the door open while they

carry him out. Then I have to get hold of Leibowitz, but
Leibowitz has turned judge, and Arthur Garfield Hays
is out of town. And then the trial and the conviction and
the pictures in the paper, and then the visit up the river,
and the last mile. It's all absorbing, stirring, and excel-
lently done, but it's not much fun, riding back alone from
Ossining with a cold friend up there.

The morning after the night that I wished he wouldn't
come, he didn't come, but there was a letter from him, one
of the nicest documents I have ever received and certainly
worth a hundred dollars.

"*Cher ami*," it said, "I have the honor to address these
few words to you, wishing to keep you informed of my
condition. I have the honor to inform you with my deep
personal regret that I will not come to America. Dishon-
esty is not my game. The money you so generously sent
to me is paid out in the most splendid of causes. I have
used it to obtain for myself and for a friend who shares
my idea, passage to Jamaica, from which isle this com-
munication is addressed to you. We have come here to
enlist in the forces of General de Gaulle. This is attested
by our pictures and the text which you will find under
them in the accompanying clipping from the Kingston
Star. It's not patriotism, *cher ami*. France has not been a
good mother to me ... But it's the quickest way to become
a man again. Please accept my respectful salutations.

André Pigueron."

171

CAMP NOMOPO

11

CAMP NOMOPO

AFTER her first walk through the city, Barbara came back to the Hotel Metropolitano in Quito with her lips blue and her little fists clenched. Mimi put her to bed and I went out to look for a garment that would shield her against the cold wind that blows down from Pichincha. There was no snow suit to be had; it's not cold enough for that, and the coats for little girls which I found and brought back to the hotel Barbara waved away. Four and a half years old, she knew exactly what she wanted. She sat up in bed with the first measles spots on her chest and said she would rather freeze to death than wear anything like the samples she had seen.

During the next weeks while she was in bed, I had to design coats for her. I exhausted myself making a stack of fashion drawings, designs of dramatic coats, and hats to go with them, and I cut paper dolls out of old fashion magazines and pasted my coats on them. The design that found favor with Barbara was a three-storied kind of pelerine, a garment such as Viennese fiacre drivers of the time of Franz Josef used to wear.

"This is it," she said. "That's the bestest good one."
As soon as Barbara was well, we went to a tailor with
the design. The shop of Señor Pablo Duque Arias faces
the square of San Francisco. It is like an indoor farm.
Chickens run around among the sewing machines and
over the low podium on which Mr. Arias's chief cutter sits
with crossed legs; a cat, a dog with offspring, and a par-
rot complete the fauna; the flora consist of artificial
paper roses stuck in a dry vase that stands on a small

shelf between an oil print of the Madonna and a picture of the Temptation of St. Anthony.

Barbara eyed this *salon de couture* with alarm and suspicion, but she let Señor Arias measure her. He studied my design and then we went to the store of Don Alfonso Perez Pallares to buy the cloth—the tailor, Barbara, Madame, and myself. We found something that looked like the lining of a good English traveling bag. It was made in Ecuador and it was agreeable to everyone.

The coat was in work for a week, and on each day we inspected progress of the garment. At the end, Barbara looked into a mirror and was delighted with the results. It cost $7.50, not counting my time and talent. The coat was a very warm and useful garment on the return trip to New York in February.

Barbara is one of the seventy-five or a hundred over-privileged children who are allowed to play inside the cast-iron confines of Gramercy Park. Another little girl, equally well fixed, is an earnest, dark-haired, five-year-old whose name is Ruthie. Ruthie played with Barbara one day and they became friends—and at their third meeting, on a day in March, when Barbara was dressed in my creation, little Ruthie said to Barbara, "You look like Oliver Twister in that coat. That's a coat like orphans wear. I think it's terrible. I don't see how you can wear it."

On a visit to Ruthie's house that afternoon, Barbara

inspected Ruthie's wardrobe. She did not wear the "Oliver Twister" coat when she came back, but carried it in her arms and hid it in the closet of her room.

She succeeded by a week of ceaseless cajolery and little-girl appeal in wangling a new winter outfit from me when it was already spring and all the Gramercy Park trees were breaking out with small green buds. Of course, it was an outfit exactly like something that Ruthie had, only newer.

Barbara and Ruthie were now bosom friends. They sat together on a bench facing a stone urn, to the left of the statue of Mr. Booth, and there they hatched another plot. The plan was to go to a summer camp together. Little Ruthie had been at this camp the year before and she described the sylvan, rugged beauty of that life to Barbara. Barbara said to Ruthie that she'd love to go but that she was afraid she would be lonesome, that she never had gone anywhere without her parents.

"Oh," said Ruthie, "after the third day you forget you ever had a father or mother."

Barbara came home with this bit of grim wisdom.

The camp we chose took care of a hundred girls. It was in the upper Adirondacks. The water came from

artesian wells, the children slept in semi-bungalows and washed themselves at ten taps that spouted cold artesian water. The taps were conveniently located in front of the bungalows, the prospectus said, and the children got up to the sound of a bugle at 7:30 a.m. and did their own housework.

When I came to this part of the booklet I was convinced that nothing was better for our darling than to rise in the upper Adirondacks at seven-thirty and scrub herself at a cold-water tap.

Barbara hopped on one foot and on the other and clasped her hands with joy when I told her that she would be one of the lucky members of Camp Nomopo, which in the language of the Indians means **Land That Is Bright.**

The equipment needed for this simple life had to be marked with the name of the child and was as follows:

Bathing suits, 2

Bathing sandals, 1 pair

Heavy bathing caps, 2

Cotton ankle socks, 4 pairs

Cotton underwear, 4 suits

Pajamas, 3 pairs

Bathrobe, 1

Tennis sneakers, 1 pair

Handkerchiefs, 6

Play suits, 2

Bedroom slippers, 1 pair

Rubbers, 1 pair

Tennis racquet, 1

Tennis balls, 3

Toilet articles

Poncho, 1

Rain hat, 1

Riding breeches, 1 pair

Bed sheets, 3

Pillow cases, 3

Dark blankets, 3

Bath towels, 3

Face towels, 3

Mattress protector, 1

Laundry bag, 1

Duffle bag, 1

Folding knife and spoon, 1 each

Drinking cup with handle, 1

Sewing material

Bible, 1

In addition, there was this special equipment:

1 pair Nomopo gabardine shorts

1 pair Nomopo brown oxfords

2 white Nomopo shirts

2 Nomopo suits

1 Nomopo green tie

1 Nomopo green sweater

2 pairs Nomopo ankle socks

The whole thing went into a green army trunk and was stowed in the back seat of the car.

The cost of going to the camp for two months was a healthy figure, about what it would take to stay at a good hotel for that time. There was a canteen. There were, besides, provisions for pocket money to buy extra things at the canteen and an additional charge for the materials used in the arts and crafts building of Camp Nomopo.

The camp was full of cheer and gladness when we arrived. The Madame who ran it received her guests with the intense charm and cordiality of a Howard Johnson hostess; the counselors hopped around, and little Ruthie, who had arrived the day before, took Barbara by the hand and led her down to their semi-bungalow, Number 5. I checked on the waterspout which was right next to it. The cabin was a loose shelter built on stilts, open to the north and south, with no windows, but large shutters that were held up by pieces of wood. In it stood six little cast-iron cots such as you see in orphanages; birds sang outside and the branches of the trees were the curtains.

In this room the floor was a row of unpainted boards through which, here and there, you could see the good earth. We also inspected the Mess Hall and the Infirmary. The counselor that had Barbara in charge showed her how to make her bed, how to sweep the floor, and how to empty the rubbish bin—three duties that were her part of the housekeeping. Barbara did it all with gusto.

The Madame came around at about 3 p.m. and said, "Please leave before it gets dark. It's easier for the child that way."

So we said good-by to Barbara. She was brave. She

said, "Good-by," and walked away with her back to the
car waving as she walked. Halfway down to shack Number 5, at the cold-water tap, she suddenly turned. The
small face was streaked with tears and she came back and
got a grip on her mother and announced that she would
not stay in the camp.

I don't know where I got the courage because my heart
was breaking, but I took Barbara, handed her to the
Madame, who pressed her to her ample bosom. I got Mimi
into the car, and drove off. We called the camp an hour

later on the phone and the Madame announced that Barbara's grief had lasted for a quarter of an hour. "Now she's in the recreation hall having the time of her life, the little darling. She's sitting in front of the big fire with little Ruthie, listening to 'Peter and the Wolf.' Don't you worry a minute about her—and please, please don't come visiting her until ten days from now."

The next day, while staying at a hotel, I reflected what a wonderful racket a children's camp is, how much better it is than owning a hotel, for example.

Imagine if the guests of a hotel like the Savoy-Plaza arrived bringing their own three dark blankets and sheets, towels, and pillow cases, made their own beds, emptied their garbage, went down to the cold-water taps in Central Park to scrub themselves, and without murmur ate the healthy, strength-giving diet you put before them! If instead of going out in the evening and spending their money in rival establishments, they would quietly sit around the bar listening to "Peter and the Wolf" or do arty-crafty things in the ballroom—all of them dressed in hats, shoes, and sweaters marked Savoy-Plaza!

We came back after ten days in which we wrote nine letters and received four cards written by Barbara's counselor. After a glowing report on how glad and happy and what a fine girl she was, the Madame sent for her.

She came in the rain, between the wet dripping trees, in the Nomopo rain hat, the Nomopo green sweater and

poncho, alone and much sadder looking than "Oliver
Twister" ever was. She broke out in streams of tears when
she saw us and she kept crying even after it stopped rain-
ing outside. She blinked red-eyed in the sun that shone
above rays of floating mist.

We went out to a play field, and, at one moment when
we stepped aside to discuss what to do, Barbara found
herself surrounded by her comrades. Madame looked down
at her with reproach and her counselor, a maiden from
whose Nomopo sweater I could hardly take my eyes, said,
"You're not going to be a sissy now, are you, and run
away from us?"

Barbara was the most complete portrait of misery I
have ever seen, not excepting the work of El Greco. She

cried, "I don't like it here. I want to go home with Mummy and Pappy. I want to go home; I don't like it here. I want to go home."

We took her into the car with us and I said in French to Mimi that I thought under the circumstances it would be the best thing to take her home with us. While I spoke, she took hold of the leather straps that are attached to the convertible top of the car as if to anchor herself, and said, "You don't have to speak French, I know what you were saying. You said, 'Let's start the car and push Barbara out and drive away like the last time' "—and then she continued, "I dream about you at night and when I wake up you're not there, and in the morning, another little girl next to me cries and that makes me cry too.

"Ruthie said she cried too the first time last year, but her mother just left her there and never came to see her and now she's used to it, but I won't get used to it because I dream of you every night. And it's so cold in the morning, and I have to empty the pail and sweep."

The washing at the tap she had got around, apparently. She was streaked with dirt and her hair was a mess. She said, "We take a bath twice a week, down at the lake, and the water is cold. I want to go home. I don't like it here. I want to go home with Mummy and Pappy."

A man came to the car and smiled and said, "I'm only the husband of Mrs. Van Cortland who runs the camp and I can assure you that Barbara's the happiest little girl when you're not here. She sings and plays all day long. I think it would be a great mistake for you to take her away."

I told him that we would take her away. Barbara let go of the straps and the man said, "Well, all I can say is that in my twenty-seven years this has happened only once before."

Barbara smelled of garlic and unwashed hair. They had had meat loaf for lunch. It was dark by the time we had made the decision and we stayed for supper. It began to rain again and there is nothing more wet and desolate than Adirondack camps in the rain. The meal was served on a drafty porch, a piece of canvas blew in with every gust of wind. The menu consisted of melted cheese poured over toast and a lukewarm rice pudding that tasted like glue; a glass of milk was served to each diner.

We left poor Ruthie behind, and the Madame and her husband assured us again that it was only the second time in twenty-seven years that such a thing had happened.

SWEET DEATH IN
THE ELECTRIC CHAIR

12

SWEET DEATH IN THE
ELECTRIC CHAIR

M ANY years ago when I worked in a famous New York hotel, I lived in one of its unoccupied apartments.

I had with me a man I had picked up on a ferryboat. He was out of a job and by profession a tailor. He pressed my suits and sometimes picked up extra money by working at odd jobs in the hotel. For a hobby he played the violin; he played it quite nicely. His name was Lustgarten.

On one of the evenings when there were no parties at the Splendide and the ballroom remained dark and empty, Lustgarten and I went to the theater.

We went to see *Lysistrata*. During the second act a loud rain began to fall outside in the street and after the curtain went down people jumped over puddles and ran, bent over, to the opened doors of taxicabs.

In a niche of the theater building, to the right of the door, pressed against the wall, stood a small boy and a larger one who held him by the neck of a torn sweater.

The little one's face was wet and smudged. He looked

up at the older boy. Under his arm, tightly squeezed, were
several mussed copies of the *Daily Mirror*.

The rain came down in a curtain of strings and splashed
on the sidewalk. Lustgarten unfurled an umbrella and
stood on his heels, and when the umbrella was opened the
larger boy moved under it, letting go of the small one. The
little fellow sold me a paper. Immediately after he had

received a nickel, he jumped out into the water and ran across the street to the second-balcony entrance of another theater. Lustgarten was pushed out into the rain as the larger boy chased after the little one. It all happened very quickly and when we got to the other side of the street, Lustgarten was almost thrown into the gutter as the bigger boy came rushing out of the balcony entrance and raced down toward Eighth Avenue.

We found the little one with two unsold copies of the *Mirror* sitting on the stairs with one shoe off. He told us that the other boy had stolen his money: the nickel he had had in his hand and, besides, the day's earnings of sixty-five cents which he had hidden in his left shoe. The thief had slashed down the front of the shoe where it was laced, pulled the shoe off, taken the money, and run.

"The dirty lousy bum," growled the little boy and picked the stubs of his shoelaces out of their eyelets. He said, with a nod in the direction of Eighth Avenue, that now he could not even go home, as a beating awaited him if he returned without money. He said that in a casual, tired fashion and when I asked him where he would sleep, he shoved his filthy cap back, pushed his lower lip out and shrugged his shoulders.

I decided then to take him home to the hotel.

Lustgarten pulled at my sleeve and shook his head. He whispered, "Give him some money, fifty cents or a dollar, and send him off—send him home in a cab if you must, but don't bring him into the hotel. Look at him. No joy will come out of this, and besides I wouldn't be surprised if the boy isn't covered with lice . . ."

A cab came along and I told the driver to take us to the hotel. Lustgarten sat in a corner and the boy, with his two copies of the *Mirror*, sat on the floor. I asked him how old he was and he said that he was eight. He answered my questions in a voice too old for a child, too young for a man; a soft husky talk like that of a young streetwalker. He smelled like an animal, like a dog. His face was a mixture of fatigue and impertinence.

Whenever we had reason to enter or leave the hotel unobserved, we used, instead of the front-entrance door or the employees' entrance, an auxiliary ballroom door at the side of the hotel on a street where the least traffic was.

It was like all the Splendide's doors, a revolving door, cumbersome to open. Revolving doors are locked with two long plungerlike rods that go up into the ceiling. The locks are high up, near the top of the door. While I lit a match, Lustgarten had to reach up and find the keyholes, turn the door, let us in, and then lock the door twice from the inside. He was annoyed that he had to do all this on account of the boy.

Teddy came into the ballroom with no manifestation of awe. He held on to his newspapers and sat in the ballroom office waiting for Lustgarten to bring him a glass of milk and a sandwich. He drank the milk, ate the sandwich, wiped his mouth with the napkin, and then we took the service elevator up to the apartment.

After he entered the living room he walked to a large sofa, put his papers on it, placed his face on them, and then he fell instantly asleep.

Lustgarten wanted to get him to take a bath but I said to leave him alone. The boy slept all night.

"You must listen to reason, Herr Graf," said Lustgarten the next morning, sitting at the side of my bed. "Who is this boy? Where does he come from? Who is going to take care of him? What if anything happens to him? What about his parents? What about if the management finds out that he is here? We'll all be thrown out. I had a brother once who took a boy like this off the street, the trouble he had! I don't even want to tell you. Give him his breakfast, give him money, give him anything you like, but send him away or you'll be sorry. No good ever comes of this kind of charity."

Teddy told me that his name was Iswolsky, that he was of Polish parentage, that he lived on Tenth Avenue and Forty-fourth Street, and that he attended a Polish parochial school in which English was taught two days a week and Polish the rest.

The boy who took his money, he said, regularly waylaid him but never had come as close to Broadway as last night. He usually waited for him down near the river.

Teddy was silent whenever Lustgarten came into the room. When I asked him whether he would like to stay with me he said, "Sure."

He was still wild and hungry looking after he was washed. His face was old, he had a certainty to all his motions. In standing, sitting, running, there was never any play, any foolish posture in his limbs, no repetition of meaningless phrases or nonsense in his talk, no loud laughter and no song. He had a bitter logical mind, and he never cried.

There was some trouble with the Polish principal when I took him out of the parochial school and placed him in a public school. The teacher came out into the street with some neighbors and shouted after the car in which I drove away with Teddy.

There was more trouble when Lustgarten had to go to a store with Teddy and buy him shoes, a turtleneck sweater, some clothes and linen. Lustgarten did not want to go with Teddy and Teddy did not want to go with Lustgarten.

A week after he was in the new school I received a card and the teacher said that she regretted to have to inform me that Teddy had appeared only twice. At the hotel he came and went very freely. He sometimes arrived at two in the morning, and several times he did not come home at all.

He had a pocketknife and besides always carried a string with a piece of lead attached to the end of it. With this apparatus he fished coins out of subway gratings. To pick up the coins he attached chewing gum to the lead. He traveled all over New York on the rear bumpers of automobiles and on the ends of trolley cars, and once he pushed some bricks from the roof of the hotel down into the street. There was a commotion but nobody was hurt. He denied doing it, but one of the maids, who was drying her hair on the roof of the hotel, told the engineer and the house detective who came up to investigate that she had seen a little boy with black hair on the roof just before the brick fell down. He spent most of his time in cheap movies, seeing the features twice. I took him along to better pictures occasionally, but he hated Chevalier, and of "Nanook of the North" he said, "Nothing but snow and whiskers." He did not enjoy the hotel's cooking and subsisted on hot dogs and hamburgers which he bought outside the Splendide.

"He is going to end up in jail," said Lustgarten. "On the gallows that boy is going to end. Just wait, your pet will make you a lot of trouble. I would like to be in charge of him. First thing every day, a good licking, whether he deserved it or not, and instead of pocket money I'd give him a slice of black bread and a smack on the head. Wait and see, you're going to be sorry."

Lustgarten wouldn't listen to any explanations or understand that to beat children is a completely European fashion of education.

Lustgarten came into the room with a triumphant face when he could at last report that a pair of studs were missing, golden ones. He said that Teddy must have stolen them. He came next with stories that small change was missing out of a box where he kept it.

The week after that report I was short a five-dollar bill. Next, two bottles of wine disappeared and a bottle of excellent Scotch. We did not know exactly when it was stolen because we had not checked up on our stock for a while.

Lustgarten came and made a speech and begged to throw Teddy out, but I told him to have patience. I explained to him that a child that has led a life like Teddy's can't be cured with a lecture or a thrashing. "First we must get his affection," I said, "then we can work on him."

Lustgarten folded his hands and shook his head, and once when he buttoned Teddy's shirt he shook and choked him. And he looked at the bottles every day.

"Aha," he said the week after we had discovered the first series of thefts and again with pleasure he announced, "Look, two more quarts of champagne, Krug 1928, extra dry, are gone. They were here yesterday."

"What interests me," I said to Lustgarten, "what I would like to know is how does he get them out of the hotel? He's such a small boy; the bottles are heavy and awkward to hide . . ."

"He doesn't have to take it out," said Lustgarten. "Most probably he sells it down in the basement. Your pet is all over the house like a mouse. You can see him in the cellar, on the roof, in every elevator. He's the butcher's and cook's friend. They make hamburgers for him. As for the wine, he sells it perhaps to a bus boy or a waiter, who in turn sells it to a captain, who sells it finally to a customer for twenty dollars a bottle. That's why we have Prohibition."

"Why can't we put a lock on the closet where the champagne is kept?" I said.

"Because the closet is a very antique and shaky Sheraton sideboard."

"Then why can't we move the champagne to a closet which can be locked?"

That is where the argument ended. Lustgarten walked away mumbling. He retired into himself for a week and he never looked at Teddy.

Toward the end of Lustgarten's silence, a man in a cheap overcoat and a derby came into the hotel and was shown to the ballroom office. He sat in a chair when I went to see him, opened his mouth and closed his eyes like a bird.

In a hotel, people like this usually have a cigar between their fingers and start their conversation with "How much do you want for the use of the Hall?" but after the rental figure is quoted them, they get up and ask for the address of the Hotel Commodore or the Pennsylvania.

But this one announced that he was a detective. He asked me whether a small boy by the name of Tommy Iswolsky lived with me. He opened his mouth again, made an effort to speak, and then said, "Where's the boy? Where is he now, I mean?"

I told him that I did not know where he was, that perhaps he was upstairs. We took an elevator to the top floor and walked down to the apartment. Teddy was not there.

"In case he comes in while I am here," said the detective with closed eyes, "in case he comes, you just sit there and listen. I don't want you to do any talking or make any signs to him, you understand? You just sit here, and I'll be here, you understand that? I'll ask all the questions."

I gave the detective a drink and talked with him and after about ten minutes Teddy came into the room.

The detective called him, placed him in front of himself so that the boy's back was turned in my direction. He took hold of both the boy's arms and he closed his eyes again and after a while he said:

"What's your name?"

"Teddy Iswolsky."

"What's this man's name?"

The boy told him my name.

"What do you call him when you talk to him?"

"I call him Chief."

"What does he call you?"

"He calls me Teddy."

"Where does he sleep?"

"In there."

"And where do you sleep?"

"In here on the sofa."

He asked a few more questions and then he said, "All right sonny, run along now and play."

The detective picked up the phone and called a number. He gave his name and said with closed eyes: "I'm here on case number so and so, and this man doesn't seem to be either a criminal or a pervert. I'll hand in my report tomorrow."

He hung up. "Sorry, Mister. I think you'll hear from the Society," he said to me. "You know you can't just pick up a stray boy and keep him. There are formalities, papers to sign, but if I were you, I'd get rid of the kid.

I've never seen it work out. Good day, sir, and thanks for the drink."

Lustgarten said: "For God's sake send that boy away. If the management hears of this—a little boy who is already a bootlegger, a thief, and you think you can do anything with him. Before anything serious happens send him away." I walked out into the foyer on my way down to the ballroom. Teddy stood next to a portière, his cap in hand, the little old face pale, the mouth clamped into a straight line. I think I wanted to say something to him, and he wanted to say something to me. I had the doorknob in my hand for a while longer than it was necessary but then I went to take the elevator to the first floor of the hotel to see that the plates for five hundred people were in their places and the waiters' fingernails clean.

I thought during the serving of the dinner that it was best to send him home. I thought that when the banquet was over, if it were not too late, I'd take him home myself. I thought about this after the soup was served. I walked out into the pantry.

Teddy stood on top of the service stairs, as he always stood at entrances, afraid to come into the room, and he sent his hungry look down at me.

The guests went home early and when I got up to the apartment, Teddy was waiting again.

I asked him to sit down next to me, and I asked him about his father and mother. He did not answer. He sat staring and then he said that his father was in prison. He said that his father was in Sing Sing.

His father, Thomas Iswolsky, he said, had killed a man. He said that he had wanted to ask me for some money so that his mother could visit him. It would take five dollars he said. He confessed that he had taken some money to help his mother. She needed it, he said, for lawyers and to visit his father. His face was pale, his eyes large and fixed on a place he had picked to look at while he talked to me, a point somewhere between the half-open doors that led to Lustgarten's pantry.

He ran home with the money about eleven o'clock.

The next evening I had to see a man who wanted to give a dinner at the hotel and who had very definite ideas about the decorations of the room and the menu. He had an office downtown and worked late. I drove down to see him at 111 Broadway. Lustgarten and Teddy waited in the car. It was about eleven at night when I got through and we drove uptown again.

We passed Madison Square at the moment when the clock on the Metropolitan Building struck eleven. Teddy sat between Lustgarten and me. Suddenly he clawed himself into my coat and screamed: "Now they're cutting his trouser leg, now they're taking him in, now they're turning on the juice. It's all over," he whimpered.

It is difficult to console anyone, and more so to help a child. After Lustgarten understood that Teddy's fa-

ther had been executed in the electric chair, he felt sorry that he had ever disliked the boy. He talked to him, took him on his lap, and when we got to the hotel he cheerfully unlocked the revolving door and took Teddy upstairs. He put him to bed and afterward walked around half the night accusing himself. He apologized and said he was sorry to have been so mean and that God would reward me for my goodness of heart. He suffered a complete emotional reverse.

Teddy was gone most of the next day and he came back and said that his mother needed a little more help. She had a small amount of insurance money coming to her, but bringing the body down from Sing Sing cost a lot of money. There were burial expenses and she needed money to put the children into proper dark clothes. He needed another twenty-five dollars, to which Lustgarten contributed an extra five.

Two days after he came and told us that the dead father had arrived. He smelled, he said, of burns. When one stood at the head of the coffin, the hair, what was left of it and not completely singed away, smelled of vinegar. He explained that they use a sponge with vinegar on it to insure quick execution.

He was dressed in a cheap suit, the dead father, a cheap suit made in prison. He described the candles and the flowers in detail.

I told Teddy that I would take the afternoon off and go home with him and see what I could do for his poor mother. At this he suddenly protested.

"Oh—please, Chief—please—don't do that. You won't like it. It's terrible," he said. "The burns, the smell, and all the people crying . . ."

I held him by the hand because he wanted to run away. I had to hold on to him all the way to the address he had given the investigator. He wanted to jump out of the taxi, and while I paid, he tried to pull himself free.

It was a windy day. Open newspapers floated down the street and ashcan covers banged.

In the hall of the house where he lived he kicked and bit, but I took him along up three flights of stairs.

There was a kitchen with laundry hanging from the ceiling, a leaden children's bathtub hung on the wall. A box filled with old shoes stood under a table and two dirty little girls searched in it for a pair to wear.

In the living room of the flat, very happy, big and alive, an honest enough man, with a black curly mustache that supported two red cheeks, sat Mr. Thomas Iswolsky, Teddy's father, eating sausages with his fingers and drinking beer. On the mantel in back of him was a kewpie doll, an American flag, a papier-mâché shepherd dog with rhinestone eyes, and several empty bottles of our wine.

In an adjoining room, graced with a crepe-paper altar, and in bed, was Teddy's mother. The father explained happily that they were soon to be parents again.

Teddy was very quiet and well behaved and I left him there.